KU-202-348

Clinical Leadership: Bridging the divide

WITHDRAWN
FROM LIBRARY

BRITISH MEDICAL ASSOCIATION

0949264

Note

Health and social care practice and knowledge are constantly changing and developing as new research and treatments, changes in procedures, drugs and equipment become available.

The authors, editor and publishers have, as far as is possible, taken care to confirm that the information complies with the latest standards of practice and legislation.

Clinical Leadership

Bridging the divide

Edited by
Emma Stanton, Claire Lemer
and
James Mountford

QUAY
BOOKS

A division of MA Healthcare Ltd

Quay Books Division, MA Healthcare Ltd, St Jude's Church, Dulwich Road, London
SE24 0PB

British Library Cataloguing-in-Publication Data
A catalogue record is available for this book

© MA Healthcare Limited 2010

ISBN-10: 1 85642 398 0
ISBN-13: 978 1 85642 398 4

All rights reserved. No part of this publication may be reproduced, stored in a retrieval system
or transmitted in any form or by any means, electronic, mechanical, photocopying, recording
or otherwise, without prior permission from the publishers

Printed by CLE, St Ives, Huntingdon, Cambridgeshire

There is nothing more difficult to carry out, nor more doubtful of success, nor more dangerous to handle, than to initiate a new order of things. For the reformer has enemies all who profit by the old order, and only lukewarm defenders in all those who would profit by the new order. This lukewarmness arises partly from fear of their adversaries who have the law in their favour; and partly from the incredulity of mankind, who do not truly believe in anything new until they have had actual experience of it.

Niccolò Machiavelli

This book is dedicated to all aspiring clinical leaders and to those who support them in service of better patient care and population health.

Contents

PART 2
What do you need to know to become an effective clinical leader?

PART 3
Practical tips for clinicians

Foreword

Professor the Lord Darzi of Denham
Professor of Surgery, Imperial College London

'Why would you want to go over to the dark side?'

Since the introduction of formalised management roles within our hospitals, around 30 years ago, any clinician that has participated in the management and leadership of their healthcare organisation will in all likelihood have heard this slightly depressing refrain from their clinical colleagues. Furthermore, I am quite certain that this is frequently a mutually held opinion, with many managerial colleagues equally suspicious and mistrusting of clinicians, particularly doctors. There are many reasons for this unhelpful 'us and them' mindset between clinical and managerial staff, but key to nearly all of them is ignorance – of each other's ways of working, each other's languages and each other's cultures, and ignorance of what motivates someone to become a dietician, a financial director, a surgeon or a chief executive. This ignorance has been propagated by education and training, which invariably has occurred in uni-professional 'silos' and has often reinforced misconception and prejudice. Healthcare delivery in the 21st century is a multiprofessional team game, and yet unlike nearly all other industries, we have frequently learnt, trained and practised away from the other professionals in our team. When we have learnt, we have frequently adopted radically different perspectives on how to deliver the same 'product' of high-quality care; clinicians have been trained to consider how best to meet the needs of the patient in front of them in the clinic, the emergency room or on the operating table and not to be concerned with a wider overview; managers have been instructed to care about financial prudence, organisational development, target achievement and business planning and not about clinical outcomes and patient experience.

Thankfully, there are positive signs that this is slowly changing, that these traditional barriers between clinical and managerial staff are being eroded. During the last three years I have been privileged to lead reviews of our healthcare system, firstly within London and subsequently within the rest of England, and what I have seen and heard has heartened me. Firstly, there is an increasing realisation by clinical staff that high-quality patient care cannot be achieved in the isolation of any individual practice but must be in the setting of a quality service, one with the patient at the very centre and with an organisational culture of perpetual improvement and patient safety. Secondly, clinical engagement is increasing and is genuine; clinical staff want not only to be involved but also to lead the teams, units, networks and organisations through which they deliver patient care. More and more managers and organisations are embracing this, by adopting managerial structures that make clinicians and managers jointly accountable for performance, necessitating cooperative working across professional domains. Thirdly, when empowered and released to do so, clinicians do not fear change but drive it, by contributing to or leading innovation, improvement and service redesign.

Despite these encouraging signs, much remains to be done if we are to create a healthcare system in which the divide between 'us and them' is bridged by clinicians and managers working together for the benefit of patients and public. The key to this paradigm shift is excellent leadership, which creates a vision that engages all staff, works across professional boundaries and ensures that patients and the public are truly involved in creating health. Throughout my period in public office, whenever I saw striking examples of innovation, significant quality improvement or outstanding clinical outcomes, it was accompanied by effective leadership. This was not only at the very top of large organisations; improvements in healthcare depend first and foremost on making a difference to the experience of patients and service users, which in turn hinges on changing the day-to-day decisions and behaviours of clinical staff. This can only occur through strong *clinical* leaders, working with patients and colleagues on the frontline.

Whilst many good clinical leaders do exist within our clinics, hospitals and communities, these individuals are at a premium, and will become increasingly so; rising public expectations, a global economic downturn, an ageing population and rapidly advancing technologies will result only in the pace of change within the NHS increasing further. If organisations are going to survive in this rapidly changing future environment, they will have to be able to adapt quickly whilst remaining focused on the NHS's key aim, which is to improve the quality of care we deliver to our patients and public. This will require exceptional clinical leaders, able to take a macroscopic view on health systems and resource allocation and with an understanding of the political, economic, social and technological drivers for change that are going to influence healthcare provision throughout their careers. Aspiring clinical leaders, many of whom have been taught little of the organisational structure of healthcare, will need to learn about the funding, governance and management that are integral to the system; but simply having knowledge and information will not be enough. Future clinical leaders will require, and will need to utilise, a range of non-technical skills to allow them to manage and lead others, not just within their specialty but also across all professional boundaries. These include creating vision and setting clear direction, together with skills in service redesign and quality improvement, adaptability, self-awareness and awareness of others, working collaboratively and networking. Furthermore, they must hold, voice and enact strong personal values and beliefs that impact positively on those around them and place the patient and public at the centre of decision-making. Finally, they will need to be supported by well-developed systems, clear lines of reporting and responsibility and by an organisational culture that provides good information and encourages its use as a vehicle for improvement of performance.

This book addresses many of these concepts. It details the knowledge, skills and behaviours required in clinical leaders, from the viewpoint of a group of exceptional junior doctors, aspiring clinical leaders and participants on NHS London's 'Prepare to Lead' scheme, of which I am very proud to be a sponsor. It is an exemplar of the benefits of multiprofessional working, with several chapters being co-produced by a doctor and a senior healthcare manager who have participated as mentees and mentors on the scheme, and this is evident in the balance, the perspective and the quality of the writing.

I am honoured to author this book's foreword; I believe it will become essential reading for any clinician who wishes to learn more about leading within the NHS and who no longer wants to work in a 'them and us' world, but rather aspires to bridge the divide and work with, alongside and through others to the benefit of us all: patients, public and staff.

Preface

When books are written, the editor generally has a well-formed idea of what he or she expects the end-product to look like. This book has had a rather different and evolutionary history. The end-product exceeds our expectations, which is entirely due to the talent and commitment of the individuals who have contributed. Great leadership rests on great passion. It is when individuals become advocates for their cause that many are spurred on to leadership. It is this commitment to a cause that allows leaders to drive change forward in spite of many ups and downs. This book is about exactly those enthusiasms; the topics for each of the following chapters have originated from the passions and interests of the authors themselves. Collectively, the chapters make up a 'guided tour' of the most important topics surrounding clinical leadership today.

This book aims to encourage and to inspire as well as to inform. It is not a textbook or an academic examination of clinical leadership. Rather, our intention is that the personal narratives of the emerging clinical leaders collected here provide support (maybe even inspiration) to others whose aim is to build an NHS which better unites clinicians' skills and knowledge to those of general managers and others to create a system that delivers high-quality care to patients every time with minimal waste.

We advocate a new paradigm for clinical leadership, one where every clinician puts improving how care is organised at the heart of what they do day in, day out. We therefore advocate an additional dimension to clinicians' professional identity: being a great clinician is also about making the organisation and the setup in which you work function better. How each clinician interprets this, of course, will depend on individual strengths and particular passions – there is no one right path or right way.

There is widespread agreement that the NHS requires outstanding leadership to continue to meet the growing healthcare needs of the population it serves. Clinicians, and therefore clinical leaders, are uniquely well placed to lead on many of these issues, because of their experience, knowledge and position. The present authors are a group of specialist registrars who were selected by NHS London to be developed through mentoring and regular workshops, with the long-term aim of creating future clinical leaders. The intention is that, through programmes such as this, the NHS in future will be 'spoilt for choice' when looking for clinical leaders.

The 'Prepare to Lead' scheme began in 2007 as a pilot for six Fellows from the Department of Biosurgery and Surgical Technology at Imperial College, London. The programme aims to develop leadership knowledge, skills and behaviours in junior doctors, and to do so alongside their clinical training. In 2008, 18 new recruits joined three of the original participants in the 'Prepare to Lead' mentoring scheme, and in 2009 a further 26 junior doctors were success-fully matched with mentors. The authors of this book are from the 2008 'Prepare to Lead' cohort. Each trainee was allocated a mentor, who is a senior NHS manager and leader, from an NHS Trust, a PCT, the Department of Health or an arm's-length body. Mentors come from both clinical and non-clinical back-grounds. A number of chapters are co-authored by mentor and mentee.

This book is unique in that it is written by junior doctors who are all pas-sionate to develop as leaders, in combination with senior leaders who have extensive experience of leadership. As Daniel Goleman (2004) puts it:

> Leaders are made as they gradually acquire, in the course of their lives and careers, the competencies that make them effective. [These] com-petencies can be learned by any leader at any time.

It is hoped that by sharing the narrative of a group of junior doctors who are participating in and who appreciate the value of clinical leadership, this book will spark a sense of possibility in the reader.

This is the story of a cohort of junior doctors who are challenging tradi-tional career paths and hierarchies and being encouraged and supported by 'the system' in the process. Each of them wants to share their expertise with others and to support others to become a leader. This book is one way of reinforcing their own development while also setting down some pointers for others who wish to turn themselves into clinical leaders. It seeks to inspire clinicians and managers from all disciplines to consider what clinical leadership means for them. The views shared in this book are those of the individual contributing authors; we do not seek to represent those of the authors' employing or spon-soring organisations. Being a leader means being brave enough to put your hand up and say what you believe. That is what each of the authors has done by offering their perspective in each chapter. Of course, this book is not com-plete, and some points covered are controversial. Despite all our best efforts, the book it is not perfect. Errors will remain (for which the editors take full responsibility). But leadership itself is never perfect or clear, and rarely is it uncontroversial. Leadership is rather about pursuing a direction which excites and which makes a difference, and being brave enough to go after things you are passionate about.

We have called this book 'bridging the divide'. As a group of junior doc-tors, we have risked failure by daring to reach out across hierarchies, speci-alities and traditional boundaries. When we have done so, we found almost invariably that we have been welcomed on the other side. This book encourages other aspiring leaders to be bold enough to bridge the divide between 'us and them' in the hope that readers will similarly find a receptive environment that encourages them to obtain and deploy the knowledge and skills which are needed to lead transformational change in the NHS.

After an introduction which discusses what we mean by clinical leadership, the book is split into three parts. First (Part 1) there is an overview of the political and economic history of healthcare to better understand the origins of the current NHS setup and to provide an insight into the workings of the Department of Health. The book then shifts gear (Part 2) to explore the range of individual skills and behaviours required for effective clinical leadership, followed in Part 3 by a discussion of the practical ways in which these can be developed and deployed. The final chapter brings together the strands to focus on what clinical leadership really means for healthcare professionals and why there is good reason to believe that we are entering a 'golden era' for clinical leadership in the NHS.

This book is not just for doctors. It has applicability for clinicians of all disciplines and professional backgrounds, for healthcare managers and for policy leaders. But there is a particular focus on doctors and medical leadership. In part, this reflects the backgrounds of the authors as doctors. But also it is because doctors, in the main, are the frontline decision makers in healthcare. Often without realising it, doctors shape how resources are spent and the direction healthcare takes. Doctors are disproportionately powerful as instigators of or resisters of change.

This said, this book is relevant to all those who are passionate about what clinical leadership means for them and for the NHS. The purpose of the NHS is to deliver great care to patients. Clinical leadership is not an end in itself; it is important because it is a vital enabler of organising to deliver higher quality, more efficient care. And so we hope that patients too, as well as managers and clinicians of all backgrounds, will find light shed on many of the conundrums of the health service throughout this book.

Reference

Goleman, D. (2004) What makes a leader? *Harvard Business Review*, January.

Acknowledgements

Oliver Warren and Penny Humphris deserve recognition for their vision and commitment to setting up, growing and developing the 'Prepare to Lead' scheme. This book is just one of many outputs from the scheme, the success of which is evident in that it is an approach already being replicated in several other regions. Oliver is a truly inspirational role-model for many junior doctors and 'leaders to be' and has demonstrated exemplary peer-leadership.

We would like to thank Mark Allen for supporting the passion behind the initial book proposal and for agreeing to publish this book. Richard Myers was extremely generous with his time and creativity. Saatchi and Saatchi are to be thanked for inspiring us through their motto: 'Nothing is impossible'.

We would also like to thank the Health Foundation, particularly Martin Marshall and Stephen Thornton, and the Nuffield Trust, particularly Jennifer Dixon and Jo Harper, for their ongoing advice and support, and specifically for helping so tangibly with the book's launch.

Each of the following chapters is the consequence of dedicated thought and energy on the part of the contributing authors. We are grateful to each of you for what you have written and what you have taught us about what can be achieved through collaborative effort. Many of the mentees are no longer 'preparing to lead', but are now leading in their own right. We hope that we will continue to meet, support and inspire each other as we tackle challenges both in London and beyond.

The success of the scheme is dependent on the hard work of Hannah Reed, Judy Butler, Margaret Murphy and Ruth Carnall at NHS London and the many senior leaders throughout the NHS who generously commit to investing time in developing the leadership potential of junior doctors. We would like this book to be seen as a way of demonstrating and sharing what we have learnt from our mentors and to say 'thank you' for teaching, challenging and inspiring us – and most of all, for believing in us.

Each of us has been nurtured over the last year by extraordinary mentors. All three of us have often benefited from the guidance and support of senior medical leaders. Sir Liam Donaldson has championed clinical leadership through his own career path and through his creation of the Clinical Advisory Scheme, designed to give junior doctors valuable skills through apprentice-style learning. Our thanks go to him for being a powerful role-model and a wonderful mentor.

In 2008, we met with our retrospective mentors – Clare Chapman and Clare Panniker, for the first time. Each has given enormously of their time: Clare Chapman has committed to meeting regularly despite also having responsibility for the other 1.4 million members of the health and social care workforce; while Clare Panniker has done the same while managing a busy District General Hospital. Each has consistently listened and responded to every question that we asked, no matter how small. Both have taught us never to let work commitments compromise relationships with family and friends and to practice healthy leadership. We want to express our thanks to them for playing devil's advocate when needed and for modelling what it means to be a great mentor as well as a successful leader, and for encouraging us to do what we enjoy and what matters.

Emma Stanton, Claire Lemer and James Mountford
London, October 2009

Participants at the NHS Prepare to Lead launch

Editors

Dr Emma Stanton is a Psychiatry Specialist Registrar, currently seconded as a Clinical Advisor to the Chief Medical Officer at the Department of Health. She became interested in leadership and teamwork after competing in the Round the World Yacht Race 2005–06. Emma is passionate about clinicians developing management and leadership skills from an early stage in their training. In 2006, Emma was a founding member of, and has subsequently Chaired, BAMMbino, the junior doctors arm of the British Association of Medical Managers. In 2009, Emma was appointed as an Emerging Leader to the National Leadership Council, chaired by the Chief Executive of the NHS. Emma has an Executive MBA from Imperial College, London.

Dr Claire Lemer works both as a Paediatric Registrar in North London, and as Operations Manager for Ophthalmology in an adjacent hospital. She developed an interest in management as a result of spending two and a half years at the Department of Health and WHO working for the Chief Medical Officer. During this time Claire developed her interest in quality improvement and patient safety and set up a leadership scheme for young doctors: 'The CMO's Clinical Advisor Scheme'. In 2004–05 Claire was a Commonwealth Fund/Health Foundation Harkness Fellow in Health Policy, based in Boston at Brigham and Women's Hospital, where she researched the effects of communication in paediatric medication safety. Claire studied undergraduate medicine at Cambridge and completed her medical training at University College and the Royal Free Medical School. She has an MD from University of London and an MPH from Harvard, and has recently completed an MBA from Oxford.

Dr James Mountford began his career as an NHS doctor before moving to McKinsey & Company's London office and healthcare practice. James's focus is how health systems and organisations can deliver safe, high-quality and efficient care through better leadership, especially by clinicians. In 2005–07, James was a Commonwealth Fund/Health Foundation Harkness Fellow in Health Policy, based in Boston at the Institute for Healthcare Improvement (IHI) and at the Institute for Health Policy, Massachusetts General Hospital

(MGH) where he researched how large, integrated American group practices organise for quality. He has a medical degree from Oxford and an MPH from Harvard.

The editorial team

Contributors

Priya Agrawal
Specialist Registrar in Obstetrics and Gynaecology; Clinical Adviser, National Patient Safety Agency; Obstetric Fellow, Harvard School of Public Health

Ben Ayres
ST4 Urology Registrar, Frimley Park Hospital, South Thames Region

Colin Bicknell
Senior Lecturer in Surgical Technology and Consultant Vascular Surgeon, Imperial College, London

David Bridle
Specialist Registrar in Adult Psychiatry; Darzi Fellow, East London NHS Foundation Trust

John Butler
Specialist Registrar in Obstetrics and Gynaecology, Royal Marsden Hospital, London; Clinical Advisor to the Medical Director of the NHS

Ruth Carnall
Chief Executive, NHS London

Clare Chapman
Director General Workforce, NHS and Social Care, Department of Health

David Colin-Thomé
National Clinical Director for Primary Care, Department of Health

Professor Paul Corrigan
Management Consultant and Executive Coach; Former Director of Commissioning Improvement and Innovation at NHS London & Senior Health Policy Adviser to Prime Minister Tony Blair

Safia Debar
GP and National Institute for Health and Research (NIHR) Fellow

Robert Elias
Chadburn Lecturer, St George's, University of London; Specialist Registrar in Renal Medicine, St George's Hospital, London

David Griffiths
Head of Clinical Leadership, Polyclinics Team, Commissioning Support for London; GP Principal, Yeo Vale Medical Practice, North Somerset

Penny Humphris
Independent Coach and Consultant; Facilitator 'Prepare to Lead', NHS London

Bob Klaber
Specialist Registrar in Paediatrics, Imperial College Healthcare NHS Trust; Fellow in Leadership and Management in Education, London Deanery

Andrew J. M. Leather
Consultant Surgeon, King's College Hospital NHS Foundation Trust; Honorary Senior Lecturer in Global Health, King's College London

Daniel Richard Leff
Walport Academic Clinical Lecturer in Surgery, Department of Biosurgery and Surgical Technology, Imperial College London

Claire Lemer
Specialist Registrar in Paediatrics; Clinical Advisor to the Chief Medical Officer, Department of Health

Leonard Marcus
Lecturer in Public Health Practice; Founding Director of the Program for Health Care Negotiation and Conflict Resolution, Harvard School of Public Health; Founding Co-Director, National Preparedness Leadership Initiative

Erik Mayer
Clinical Lecturer in Surgery and Specialist Registrar in Urology, Imperial College, London

James Mountford
Health Foundation/Harkness Fellow

Catherine Sheehan
Specialist Registrar in Anaesthetics, Queen Charlotte's Hospital, London

Rebecca Syed Sheriff
Specialist Registrar in Psychiatry, Maudsley Hospital; Honorary Research
Fellow, Institute of Psychiatry

Emma Soane
Senior Lecturer, London School of Economics

Emma Stanton
Psychiatry Specialist Registrar, South London and Maudsley NHS Foundation
Trust; Clinical Advisor to the Chief Medical Officer, Department of Health

Benjamin M. Thomas
Specialist Registrar in Anaesthetics, North West Thames (Imperial)

Oliver Warren
Surgical Registrar, North West Thames; Clinical Lead, 'Prepare to Lead'
Scheme, NHS London

Claire Woolcock
Consultant Psychiatrist, Central and North West London NHS Foundation
Trust

Clinical leadership – the what, why and how

David Griffiths, Catherine Sheehan, Safia Debar, Ben Ayres and David Colin-Thomé

Successful organisations have strong and effective leaders. Within healthcare there is growing evidence of a link between clinical engagement and organisational performance. Historically, there have been low levels of medical engagement with leadership and there have often been tensions between doctors and managers. One of the reasons for this is that medical training has traditionally focused squarely on developing clinical expertise rather than the teamworking, managerial or leadership skills which are specifically discussed later on in this book (Parts 2 and 3). Encouraging stronger leadership from clinicians has huge potential to improve the quality of healthcare across the NHS. At a senior level, there is an acknowledgement that managerial competencies are required for clinicians to be truly effective practitioners, and an explicit aim that some clinicians will go on to take formal service leadership roles.

> The complementary skills of leadership and 'followership' need to be incorporated into doctors' training to support professionalism. (Royal College of Physicians (2005) *Doctors in Society: Medical Professionalism in a Changing World*)

For many, this will require a significant culture shift: the current 'them and us' attitude that many clinicians have with regard to hospital management will have to evolve substantially. It is a divide that this book seeks to bridge. Too often, formal involvement in management by doctors is seen by their colleagues as crossing to the 'dark side' – an unhelpful view, but one which is a product of the way leadership and management have been approached in the NHS until recently.

Leadership by clinicians is set to become an increasingly respected and sought-after quality, particularly in the light of the 'Next Stage Review' (Darzi, 2008) and subsequent policy developments. This book aims to provide an overview of the fundamentals of what it means to be a clinical leader and considers practical steps that clinicians can take to nurture and develop their leadership potential.

This introduction first sets out the definitions that are used throughout the rest of the book, and then explores the difference between leadership and management. It also outlines some barriers that have traditionally held back clinical leaders with aspirations to lead their organisations or the system itself more widely.

Definitions of leadership

Before examining 'clinical leadership', the definition of 'leadership' in general should first be examined. There is no universally accepted single definition of 'leadership'. It means different things to different people in different contexts. Common themes include exerting influence over the thoughts, attitudes and behaviours of others, setting a direction, motivating and inspiring, helping others realise their potential, leading by example, selflessness and making a difference.

The dictionary definition of leadership below focuses on position (singular or collective). It does not refer to the individual qualities which may make a leader successful or unsuccessful.

> *1. The position or function of a leader. 2. The period during which a person occupies the position of leader: 'during her leadership very little was achieved'. 3. a. the ability to lead. b. (as modifier): leadership qualities. 4. the leaders as a group of a party, union, etc.: 'the union leadership is now very reactionary' (Collins English Dictionary, 1991)*

Peter Drucker (1996), in the Foreword to the Drucker Foundation's *The Leader of the Future*, tells us:

> *The only definition of a leader is someone who has followers.*

In the *21 Irrefutable Laws of Leadership*, John Maxwell (2002) sums up his definition of leadership as:

> *Leadership is influence – nothing more, nothing less.*

This begins to define what leaders actually do, which can also be thought of as (to take Wikipedia's definition, 2009):

> The process of social influence in which one person is able to enlist the aid and support of others in the accomplishment of a common task

By contrast, Warren Bennis' (1989) definition of leadership is focused much more on the personal attributes of leaders:

Leadership is a function of knowing yourself, having a vision that is well communicated, building trust among colleagues, and taking effective action to realize your own leadership potential.

The above examples illustrate that there are many ways to look at leadership. A succinct yet resonant definition that contains the key element of shaping what others do comes from former US President Dwight Eisenhower:

Leadership is the art of getting someone else to do something you want done because he wants to do it.

Definitions of leadership are heavily influenced by the context in which leadership is taking place. Thus it is likely that clinicians would look at Eisenhower's definition and identify strongly with it, yet many would, in the same breath, denounce their own leadership skills. For the majority of clinicians today, 'leadership' refers to a few individuals heading organisations rather than the more distributed leadership of day-to-day clinical practice. It is this latter sense of 'leadership by all' which this book embraces and aims to nurture and develop.

Leadership versus management

The terms *leadership* and *management* are often used interchangeably, but there are important differences: managers work within a system to maintain existing goals and direction. They use people and equipment within the existing structure to meet a goal, or they use a process to produce results. By contrast, a leader's main function is to set the direction and vision for projects. Leaders may look to build new relationships and working structures, gaining commitment from the people in the organisation. One of their main skills is motivating and inspiring others. So, whereas leaders ask themselves 'Where are we going?' managers tend to ask 'How do we get there?'.

Warren Bennis (1989) summarises the differences with twelve distinctions between managers and leaders:

- The manager administers; the leader innovates.
- The manager is a copy; the leader is an original.
- The manager maintains; the leader develops.

- The manager focuses on systems and structure; the leader focuses on people.
- The manager relies on control; the leader inspires trust.
- The manager has a short-range view; the leader has a long-range perspective.
- The manager asks how and when; the leader asks what and why.
- Managers have their eyes on the bottom line; leaders have their eyes on the horizon.
- The manager imitates; the leader originates.
- The manager accepts the status quo; the leader challenges it.
- The manager is the classic good soldier; the leader is his own person.
- The manager does things right; the leader does the right thing.

While it is true that some individuals may have a natural aptitude (or appetite) for one more than the other, leadership and management are certainly not mutually exclusive – it is rare to get one in pure form without the other. Great leaders can be great managers and vice versa, which is fortunate since it is unlikely that an individual will work in a leadership position without also having a managerial aspect to the role.

What is *clinical* leadership?

This refers to anyone in a clinical role who exercises leadership. The term originated from nurses who became managers, but it has grown into a more generalised definition that encompasses anyone with a clinical background who occupies a leadership role.

In *Our NHS, Our Future* (2007) the Department of Health describes the essence of clinical leadership as:

> To motivate, to inspire, to promote the values of the NHS, to empower and to create a consistent focus on the needs of the patients being served. Leadership is necessary not just to maintain high standards of care, but to transform services to achieve even higher levels of excellence.

Meanwhile, the *McKinsey Quarterly*, in a recent article on clinical leadership, used the following definition:

> Clinical leadership is putting clinicians at the heart of shaping and running clinical services, so as to deliver excellent outcomes for patients and populations, not as a one-off task or project, but as a core part of clinicians' professional identity.

For this book, the working definition of clinical leadership is:

Empowering clinicians to have the confidence and capability to continually improve health care on both the small and the large scale.

This definition is deliberately broad, in order to include all those who are involved in formal clinical management and leadership roles, but also to include clinicians who do *not* occupy formal positions in a hierarchy but who nonetheless work systematically to improve the quality and efficiency of the service they deliver.

Clinical leadership: the past

It may be helpful to consider why clinicians have not always been at the heart of NHS leadership. The original model for the NHS was a centralised administration (the government and Department of Health) with clinicians acting peripherally to manage patients' healthcare according to their professional judgement (see Chapter 2). Although budgets were set centrally, clinicians were able to decide which patients got what and when at a local level.

As healthcare became more expensive and the NHS budget became severely stretched in the 1980s, significant thought went into how to exercise more control over costs. The Griffiths Report into NHS management structures suggested that clinicians should '*accept management responsibility*' in order to maintain clinical autonomy. This led to the development of the present structure with clinical directors, who tend to continue doing some front-line clinical work while also occupying formal leadership positions.

Healthcare organisations, particularly hospitals, tend to be 'professional bureaucracies'. Unlike 'machine bureaucracies' where a hierarchical structure sees senior management exert control over their staff (for example, as in a factory), healthcare has a more tribal culture. Front-line staff tend to be highly trained and hold strong opinions. They exert control by virtue of their specialist knowledge, and by peer pressure or collegial influence. As the staff on the 'shop floor' may consider themselves to have more direct experience and relevant knowledge than their managers, professional bureaucracies such as healthcare are often particularly resistant to change. Certainly in such a setup it is hard, if not impossible, for managers to impose changes to which the front-line are opposed.

Clinical leadership has been proposed as a possible bridge across the divide between 'them and us'. In the USA, Kaiser Permanente has been the archetype for successfully involving clinicians in leadership and managerial roles. The turnaround of the Veteran's Health Administration (VA), also in the USA, is a similar story. The VA was a struggling organisation failing to attract staff and delivering poor-quality care with unsustainable finances. Faced with the risk of imminent closure, Ken Kizer – himself a doctor – rebuilt the VA into an organisation that is now widely seen as a desirable place both to receive healthcare and to work. One of his key strategies was focusing on local provision and decision-making, concentrated around the patient. He introduced an electronic health record and systems to measure performance (quality, access, satisfaction, cost-effectiveness, return to daily activities/functions and community health). He understood that the key to success was leadership in terms of the model he set and creating systems that allowed others, particularly clinicians, to lead. In the UK, some forward-thinking organisations have also found that giving power and responsibility to respected practising clinicians has increased engagement in the management of change.

However, even in high-performing trusts, there exists a tendency to involve only the relatively small group of senior clinicians working in management positions. It is clear that even in leading NHS trusts, widespread clinical engagement, let alone leadership, is not yet commonplace.

Barriers to clinical leadership

An examination of the past is only complete if the barriers to change are clearly identified. Some of the barriers to change are structural while others are reinforced by outmoded training and education approaches (see Chapter 7). It is still perfectly possible for many clinicians to travel through their entire training without contemplating management or leadership. This is in stark contrast to many other organisations (ironically including the NHS management training scheme) which tend to fast-track an 'elite' group of high-potential leaders onto intensive educational programmes and placements.

The approach, until recently, would seem to follow from a belief that, on appointment to a consultant position, doctors automatically acquire the capabilities to take on leadership roles. Despite the lack of systematic leadership development, many doctors have succeeded in these roles. But this approach is strikingly at odds with how other industries approach management and leadership development. Rather than relying on the heroic and unusual efforts of the few, success is better built through clear systems being put in place to assist the majority.

All too often, the only involvement in building these core skills is a last-minute course in management before interviewing for consultant posts. Courses are often attended in a 'sheep-dip' fashion out of necessity to tick the correct box. Even those who do attend courses or have the opportunity to be involved in management or leadership have to battle deeply ingrained educational norms. Clinical training values analysis and scientific rigour, rather than embracing the creativity, innovation and strategic insight required for successful leadership and management. And yet being an NHS consultant involves considerable amounts of management and leadership.

Perhaps worse still is that those junior clinicians who aspire to make changes are often actively discouraged from doing so by the rigid, hierarchical structure of the current system. Yet it is junior members of clinical teams who are most frequently and directly exposed to the current problems in front-line care; they are often most likely to have ideas for improvements and innovation.

Does clinical leadership training work? The Royal College of Nursing evaluated their Clinical Leadership Programme and reported a positive change in leadership capabilities, with increased confidence and greater optimism about personal clinical roles. This was associated with increased commitment to improving patient care and team effectiveness. Nurses at the Royal Brompton and Harefield Trust have brought about change through patient-centred leadership (Chantler, 1999). As a specific example, empowered clinical leaders developed an education campaign to stop interruptions during drug rounds, which resulted in fewer drug errors. Empowering clinicians at a departmental level within hospitals can also lead to financial savings. For example, as long ago as 1985, Guy's Hospital in London decentralised budgets to clinical directorates and found savings of 15% with no reduction in the quality or quantity of patient care.

Above are just a few examples, from a growing set of such stories, of how front-line clinical staff can make a profound difference when given the opportunity to drive change. Yet many argue that a further barrier is the lack of good role models. Not because such individuals do not exist, but rather that they are too often lacking in visibility and prominence. Instead of being celebrated for their success, these individuals are frequently vulnerable to criticism. The National Leadership Council (set up in 2009) seeks to overcome this barrier and promote individual leadership success stories through the presentation of annual NHS Leadership Awards.

A profound philosophical barrier also prevents involvement. There is a feeling amongst some clinicians that they should be advocates for their patients and should make treatment decisions on clinical grounds, remaining independent of financial and political concerns; and thus involvement in management or leadership is seen to stand in direct opposition to this. Similarly, there may be conflicting interests between clinicians' own departments and practices and their umbrella organisations. This is particularly true in primary care where GP partners have to balance the needs of their patients, their Primary Care Trust (PCT) and their own businesses and personal income. Ultimately, this tension can be encapsulated as the competing demands of doing the best for the patient, doing the best for the population, and meeting the needs of the organisation and its staff. It is quite rightly a serious dilemma for many committed doctors. Perhaps the best answer to this is to remember that all clinical decisions have effects on the health system; better therefore to act with the knowledge that your actions will impact the wider system than to ignore this reality. If clinicians start to think like this, then the transition to a more active role in management or indeed leadership might look less like bridging a chasm, and more like shifts along a spectrum.

David Colin-Thomé, National Clinical Director of Primary Care and an author of this chapter, discusses how the realisation that management can directly benefit individual patients took him into clinical leadership:

> I became 'infected' by management in the 1980s when, as a local councillor, I led a review of a particularly cost-ineffective service. It made me think why I was not applying similar principles to the general practice in which I worked..., so I volunteered to be the managing partner of the practice (agreed to with alacrity by the rest of the doctors!). We defined what our aim was, got tough on ineffective practice and developed plans for better care in particular for those with long-term conditions. But where were the resources to better serve our individual patients and to take a public health focus for our registered list of patients?
>
> Then along came fund-holding providing us with a budget for wider aspects of our patients care and yet many of us were uncertain of where the then government's 'internal market' was leading us. A senior NHS manager came to see us to say 'why not go for fund-holding?' as it would provide the budget to deliver care as we envisaged. He was right. We could manage a budget for our population better than our health authority. And we did, not least by challenging ineffective and inappropriate clinical practice within and without the practice, and there was and still remains much of such clinical practice. And the resources and better services flowed.

This view is increasingly espoused in key policies such as the General Medical Council's *Management for Doctors* (2006):

> All practising doctors are responsible for the use of resources: many will also lead teams or be involved with the supervision of colleagues: and most will work in managed systems.... Doctors have responsibilities to their patients, employers and those who contract their services. This means that doctors are managers and are managed.

The challenge then, which this book seeks to address, is how to take this increasingly accepted concept of medical professionalism and make it fly in the day-to-day actions and beliefs of front-line clinicians.

Part of the challenge involves overcoming perceptions that this part of a clinician's role is either not valued or less valued than the clinical interaction. Leadership roles are often less well paid than clinical work, especially private work. Leadership may be viewed negatively by peers, commanding less respect than research or clinical achievements. In part this may arise because clinicians value autonomy highly. Thus, to many, management suggests restraint of autonomy. Where clinical leadership has been most effective, such as in Kaiser or the VA, it is clear that it acts by empowering clinicians, allowing them to define the strategy and direction for their specialty.

A further iteration of the negative perception of management and leadership is expressed in the colloquialisms applied to those stepping from the clinical world to that of management, described as 'going to the dark side' or 'sleeping with the enemy'. From early on in undergraduate training, an 'us and them' divide emerges between clinicians and managers, often subtly (or not so subtly) reinforced by professional role models in lectures and on the wards. With career progression, this outlook all too often becomes more deeply entrenched through top-down targets and rotating managers, unfamiliar with the 'real NHS', holding a view of healthcare professionals as resources. Many clinicians regard budgets and bureaucracy as illegitimate. A detailed study of leadership in an NHS hospital in the 1990s by Paul Bate showed that consultants did not accept the legitimacy of management, and as a result tried to undermine managerial power. It is equally clear that there has been a profound realisation that this is unsustainable and that success in healthcare means rising above professional barriers and embracing multi-professional working. This is something that can be best achieved by carrying into effect NHS Medical Director Sir Bruce Keogh's suggestions for altering doctors' hierarchy of affiliations. If all healthcare workers felt allegiance first to the *organisation* in its aim of delivering excellent patient care efficiently, rather than to 'tribe' or profession, much of this negative stereotyping would melt away.

This does not mean that there are not different challenges facing different professions within healthcare. Nursing, for example, has clearly created a norm in which management involvement is to be striven for. Promotion and career progression in nursing have for some time taken nurses by default away from patients and into clinical leadership roles. To date, this has not been the case for doctors within the NHS.

NHS leadership: the future

The *NHS Plan* (Department of Health, 2000) puts clinical leadership at its core:

Delivering the Plan's radical change programme will require first class leaders at all levels of the NHS.

In 2000, the NHS realised that it had some outstanding leaders, but that clinical leaders were in short-supply for the top roles. The proposed solution was to develop innovative training pathways for a 'new generation of managerial and clinical leaders', replacing the previous 'ad-hoc and incoherent' processes.

There were promises of management support and training to equip individuals for leadership tasks. A new Leadership Centre was established to provide tailored support for clinicians and managers with leadership potential at all stages of their careers.

It also promised to adapt work-based development programmes for staff at social care organisations and patient advocate and liaison services, as well as for health visitors and community nurses. These would provide them with the skills and expertise to work with and support representatives of the local community and improve health.

Following on from the *NHS Plan*, the *Next Stage Review* (2008) made it clear that:

Creating high quality workplaces requires great leadership and good management.

The *Next Stage Review* proposed that all NHS providers would be encouraged to give clinicians 'more control over budgets and HR decisions'. The experience of Kaiser Permanente in the USA inspired the concept that 'Clinicians will be encouraged to be practitioners, partners and leaders in the NHS'. The report also stated 'Clinicians are expected to offer leadership and, where they have appropriate skills, take senior leadership and management posts in research, education and service delivery'. With this in mind, the report proposed that senior clinical leadership within Strategic Health Authorities (SHAs) should be enhanced through the appointment of new, dedicated SHA Medical Directors. There was a commitment to ensuring 'that the undergraduate curricula for all medical and nursing students reflect the requirement for leadership skills in the NHS', with other healthcare professionals' training similarly boosted. SHAs were encouraged to offer Clinical Leadership Fellowships with time dedicated to enhancing leadership skills; such opportunities are discussed further in Chapter 8.

The NHS National Leadership Council was established in April 2009, chaired by the NHS Chief Executive (two of the authors of this book sit on the Council as 'Emerging Leaders'). Efforts to encourage leadership will only succeed if accompanied by a paradigm shift in thinking by clinicians towards management and leadership. It must become part of what it means to be a great clinician, not an optional extra. Until there is a groundswell of clinicians who embrace these goals as part of their everyday practice, we cannot say that clinical leadership is mature and embedded.

Clearly, the *Next Stage Review* demonstrates a commitment to bolstering leadership through undergraduate curricula and postgraduate training programmes. This is timely as, according to the National Trainee Survey in 2006, only 25% of SpRs had received *any* leadership training. A joint venture between the Academy of Medical Royal Colleges and the NHS Institute for Innovation and Improvement, *Enhancing Engagement in Medical Leadership*, started in 2006 to tackle this lack of training. The project's stated aims were to 'create a culture of greater medical engagement in management and leadership with all doctors at every level' and to increase the contribution of doctors in the transformation of services, from planning through to delivery.

One of the key goals was to develop a Medical Leadership Competency Framework, which was designed to apply to all medical students and doctors, from an undergraduate level all the way through postgraduate training and on into career-grade roles (see Chapter 7). Under this model, all medical students would be expected to achieve an appropriate level of competence, and would have exposure to management and leadership much earlier in their training. Engaging all future doctors and continuing to reinforce the value of shared clinical leadership throughout their careers will first lead to greater awareness and later will increase the pool of medical managers and leaders able take on roles in the future.

This fits in with the vision that Professor Sir John Tooke, who led the inquiry into 'Modernising Medical Careers', set out in his 2008 publication, *Aspiring to Excellence*:

> The doctor's frequent role as head of the healthcare team and commander of considerable clinical resource requires that greater attention is paid to management and leadership skills regardless of specialism. An acknowledgement of the leadership role of medicine is increasingly evident. Role acknowledgement and aspiration to enhanced roles be they in subspecialty practice, management and leadership, education or research is likely to facilitate greater clinical engagement.

As well as the competency framework, the Enhancing Engagement in Medical Leadership team also investigated the correlation between medical engagement and organisational performance. It also looked at international models of medical educational development and leadership. Of course, none of this is confined to the NHS or even to the health systems of developed countries; leadership for global health is discussed in Chapter 13.

In January 2009, *Inspiring Leaders: Leadership for Quality* set out in even greater detail the framework within which clinicians will be able to gain leadership skills and experience in the NHS. As NHS Chief Executive David Nicholson states in his introduction:

> The NHS is only just beginning to grasp the importance of leadership. We have not systematically identified, nurtured and promoted talent and leadership. While we have fantastic and talented leaders in the NHS, to take us to the next stage we need to embrace more people with different skills and backgrounds and support the development of healthcare staff in a sustained way.

This document makes it clear that the Department of Health will hold SHAs to account over their leadership development performance. Each SHA will have to 'describe how talent and leadership plans will be produced' and how they will approach 'the cultural change required'. The balance of demand and supply of suitable individuals will need to be managed to identify and plug gaps over the next five years.

Given this degree of awareness and investment, there has never been a better time for clinicians to aspire to leadership roles in the NHS. With significant organisational change occurring, this book advocates that becoming directly involved is an integral and key component of improving patient care. Leadership should not be viewed as separate from front-line clinical roles.

Embracing leadership and management as core to clinicians' day-jobs so that these functions become part of clinicians' professional identity will not be easy. It requires that clinicians come to see the effective functioning of their department and organisation as of similar importance to their own clinical skills and one-to-one interaction with patients. Change of this kind is not easy. It will take years, and will include setbacks on the journey. It will not happen without a receptive environment, at both local and wider system level. But both locally and nationally, opportunities are increasingly available for able and willing clinicians to step up into important leadership roles.

References and further reading

Adair, J. (1983) *Effective Leadership: a Self-development Manual*. Gower, Aldershot.

Bass, B. M. (2002) Cognitive, social and emotional intelligence of transformational leadership: efficacy and effectiveness. In: R. E. Riggio, S. E. Murphy and F. J. Pirozzolo (eds.) *Multiple Intelligences and Leadership*. Lawrence Erlbaum, Mahwah NJ.

Bate, P. (2000) Changing the culture of a hospital: from hierarchy to networked community. *Public Administration*, **78**, 485–512.

Bennis, W. (1989) *On Becoming a Leader*. Perseus Books, Massachusetts.

Berwick, D., Ham, C. and Smith, R. (2003) Would the NHS benefit from a single, identifiable leader? An email conversation. *British Medical Journal*, **327**, 1421–4.

Chantler, C. (1999) The role and education of doctors in the delivery of health care. *Lancet*, **353**, 1178–81.

Chantler, C. (2002) The second greatest benefit to mankind? *The Lancet*, **360**, 1870–7.

Collins (1991) *Collins English Dictionary*, 3rd edn. HarperCollins, London.

Coombes, R. (2005) Gap between NHS policy makers and doctors is 'enormous'. *British Medical Journal*, **330**, 1468.

Darzi, A. (2008) *High Quality Care for All: NHS Next Stage Review Final Report*. Department of Health, London.

Department of Health (2000) *NHS Plan*. Stationery Office, London.

Department of Health (2007) *Our NHS, Our Future: NHS Next Stage Review Interim Report*. Stationery Office, London.

Department of Health (2009) Inspiring leaders: leadership for quality. http://www.dh.gov.uk/en/Publicationsandstatistics/Publications/PublicationsPolicyAndGuidance/DH_093395 (accessed 5 April 2009).

Department of Health and Social Security (1983) *Griffiths Report: NHS Management Inquiry*. DHSS, London.

Drucker, P. F. (1996) Foreword. In: F. Hesselbein, M. Goldsmith and R. Beckhard (eds.) *The Leader of the Future: New Visions, Strategies and Practices for the Next Era*. John Wiley & Sons, New York.

General Medical Council (2006) *Management for Doctors*. http://www.gmc-uk.org/guidance/current/library/management_for_doctors.asp (accessed 7 March 2009).

Ham, C. and Dickinson, H. (2008) *Engaging Doctors in Leadership: What We Can Learn from International Experience and Research Evidence?* NHS Institute for Innovation and Improvement. http://www.library.nhs.uk/Improvement/ViewResource.aspx?resID=310504 (accessed 15 April 2009)

Ham, C., Kipping, R. and McLeod, H. (2003) Redesigning work processes in health care: lessons from the National Health Service. *The Milbank Quarterly*, **81**, 415–39.

Hamilton, P., Spurgeon, P., Clark, J., Dent, J. and Armit, K. (2008) *Engaging Doctors: Can Doctors Influence Organisational Performance?* http://www.institute.nhs.uk/images//documents/BuildingCapability/Medical_Leadership/49794_Engaging_Doctors.pdf (accessed 2 April 2009).

Hesselbein, F., Goldsmith, M. and Beckhard, R. (1996) *The Leader of the Future: New Visions, Strategies and Practices for the Next Era*. John Wiley & Sons, New York.

Hiscock, M. and Shuldham, C. (2008) Patient centred leadership in practice. *Journal of Nursing Management*, **16**(8), 900–4.

Institute for Healthcare Improvement/American Hospital Association. *Strategies for Leadership: Patient- and Family-Centered Care Toolkit*. http://www.ihi.org/IHI/Topics/PatientCenteredCare/PatientCenteredCareGeneral/Tools/StrategiesforLeadershipPatientandFamilyCenteredCareToolkit.htm (accessed 29 April 2009).

Kenmore, P. (2008) Stretch to the board. *Guardian Society*, 20 March. http://www.guardian.co.uk/society/2008/mar/20/nhs.boards (accessed 6 March 2009).

Klein, R. (2006) *The New Politics of the NHS*, 5th edn. Radcliffe Publishing, Oxford.

Large, S., MacLeod, A., Cunningham, G. and Kitson, A. (2005) *A Multiple Case Study Evaluation of the RCN Clinical Leadership Programme in England.* RCN Institute, London.

Maxwell, J. (2002) *The 21 Irrefutable Laws of Leadership Workbook.* Thomas Nelson Publishers, Nashville.

Mintzberg, H. (1979) *The Structuring of Organisations: a Synthesis of the Research.* Prentice Hall, New Jersey.

Mountford, J. and Webb, C. (2009) When clinicians lead. *McKinsey Quarterly,* February.

NHS Institute for Innovation and Improvement (2007) Enhancing Engagement in Medical Leadership. http://www.institute.nhs.uk/building_capability/enhancing_engagement/enhancing_engagement_in_medical_leadership.html (accessed 5 March 2009).

NHS Institute for Innovation and Improvement, Academy of Medical Royal Colleges (2008) *Medical Leadership Competency Framework,* 2nd edn. http://www.institute.nhs.uk/images/documents/MLCF%20May%202009.pdf (accessed 15 April 2009).

O'Dowd, A. (2007) Carruthers report calls for doctors to be more involved in NHS change. *British Medical Journal,* **334,** 499.

Perlin, J. B. (2006) Transformation of the US Veterans Health Administration. *Health Economics, Policy and Law,* **1,** 99–105.

Postgraduate Medical Education Training Board (2006) *National Trainee Survey 2006 – Key Findings.* http://www.pmetb.org.uk/uploads/media/NationalTraineeSurvey-SummaryReport_02.pdf (accessed 1 March 2009).

Powell, J. E. (1966) *A New Look at Medicine and Politics.* Pitman Publishing, Tunbridge Wells.

Quinn Mills, D. (2005) *Leadership: How to Lead, How to Live.* MindEdge Press, Massachusetts.

Royal College of Physicians (2005) *Doctors in Society: Medical Professionalism in a Changing World.* http://www.rcplondon.ac.uk/pubs/brochure.aspx?e=75 (accessed 12 April 2009).

Shapiro, J. and Smith, S. (2003) Lessons for the NHS from Kaiser Permanente. *British Medical Journal,* **327,** 1241–2.

Tooke, J. (2008) *Aspiring to Excellence: Final Report of the Independent Inquiry into Modernising Medical Careers.* http://www.mmcinquiry.org.uk/draft.htm (accessed 8 March 2009).

Wikipedia (2009) *Leadership.* http://en.wikipedia.org/wiki/Leadership (accessed 7 May 2009).

Zaher, C. A. (1996) Physician leadership. Learning to be a leader. *Physician Exec.,* **9,** 10–17.

PART I

Overview of healthcare in Britain – from before the NHS to today

This first section provides the reader with the contextual setting of the system they work for. Too few of those working in the NHS today have a solid appreciation of the wider structures of the NHS or the paths that have led to the current situation.

> Those who cannot remember the past are condemned to repeat it.
>
> *George Santayana*

Successful leadership is about learning from different sources, and we would be unwise not to look to history to inform our current priorities. This section of the book considers the distant past, the less distant past and the present day of healthcare in the UK. This is not meant to be an exhaustive history of healthcare; rather, it aims to give a flavour of some of the challenges which previous generations have faced, to set current issues in context and to show that many of the problems faced today are not new. This section is also meant to inspire. Medicine has come a long way from the practices not just of Babylonian times, but also from those of much of the 20th century.

Today's challenges are very real. Every day brings new advances and discoveries, and the pressure on healthcare to adapt quickly to these changes only increases as the pace of innovation rises and as the public's knowledge and expectations grow. An equally important theme emerging from this section is that the meaning of medical professionalism has shifted over the years; so the identity and role of 'doctor' is not fixed, but rather something that changes over time. Looking at the past, therefore, provides encouragement that today's professional paradigm can shift to embrace clinical leadership as a natural part of being a great clinician.

CHAPTER I

Medicine before the NHS

John Butler

Introduction

This chapter explores the early days of medicine and addresses two main themes. Firstly, that many of today's challenges have been seen in the past, and secondly, how the role of the clinician has evolved and adapted to the changing environment.

People in industrialised nations have never lived as long or been as healthy as they are today. In the last 100 years the advances in science and medical knowledge have been and continue to be extraordinary. Throughout history, healers and doctors have been highly valued and respected, despite often being able to do very little of actual therapeutic value, and indeed often doing more harm than good. It is paradoxical that at the same time as advances in medical knowledge and treatments are at their fastest, clinical practice is being challenged and criticised more than ever. Alongside advances in medical treatments, the growing costs of medicine and social welfare have become a major economic burden.

This chapter outlines the developments in medicine, society, and the state that laid the foundations for the creation of the National Health Service discussed in Chapter 2.

Ancient medicine

There is evidence of the recognition of disease and specific individuals consulted for its treatment since ancient times when healers were called upon to address both spiritual and physical ailments. The Babylonian law code of Hammurabi (1792–1750 BC) details not only the fees due to a healer depending on both the operation and status of the patient, but also the punishments for failure.

The roots of modern Western Medicine lie in the *Hippocratic Corpus*, a collection of Greek medical writings written between 420 BC and 370 BC setting out the famous Hippocratic Oath. The expected behaviour and practice included not harming or killing a patient, and caring for them to the best of one's ability, as well as highlighting the importance of patient confidentiality, not abusing the position of power, and teaching others in the art of medicine – guidance as familiar and relevant today as over 2000 years ago.

The eighteenth century – medical markets and new hospitals

In the United Kingdom, before the National Health Service was created in 1948, doctors competed not only against each other but also against alternative providers to attract patients, and through them, income. In eighteenth-century England there were about 3,000 recognised medical practitioners and thousands more who made all or part of their living from providing treatments. These included blacksmiths and farriers who set bones and drew teeth, and pedlars and grocers who sold drugs and folklore remedies.

The formal medical profession by the end of the eighteenth century comprised three main branches: physicians, apothecaries and surgeons. University-educated, the members of the Royal College of Physicians (founded 1518) were the medical aristocracy. They cared for affluent patients, often having to accommodate the whims and eccentricities of their moneyed clients. Physicians prescribed but did not dispense and prepare medicines. This was considered manual work, reserved for members of the Society of Apothecaries (founded in 1617), which had originated from the Grocers' Company. By contrast, surgeons were historically trade apprentices and originally members of the Company of Barber Surgeons (founded in 1540). They became the Company (eventually Royal College) of Surgeons in 1745. Surgeon-Apothecaries were forerunners of the present day General Practitioner, providing medical care and drugs to those who could pay, and together with the physicians offering some *gratis* work for charity cases. This distinction between physician and barber-surgeon lives on to this day in the use of the title 'Mr' for the surgeon.

Continental European city states, such as those of Renaissance Italy, employed town physicians and set up Health Boards in response to plague outbreaks. However, England lacked any formal health bureaucracy until the nineteenth century. The poor laws of the sixteenth and seventeenth centuries gave welfare rights to subjects within their own parish. Parish councils used ratepayers' money to provide medicines, food, and surgeons' fees. In some areas a general practitioner was contracted to receive an annual sum to treat the paupers of a parish.

Prior to the eighteenth century, there were few hospitals in England. The largest were London's two ancient hospitals of St Thomas' and St Bartholomew's. Following the foundation of the Westminster (1720) and Guy's (1724) the rest of the century saw widespread hospital building both in London and other urban centres across Britain. These hospitals were founded by enlightened benefactors to help the 'deserving poor', but not for Poor Law paupers, and could offer only a small fraction of the care needed. 'Care' usually meant food, bed-rest and convalescence for predominantly minor complaints. Severe cases of infection were often excluded from the hospital to prevent disease spreading. Dispensaries began to be established in the eighteenth century, providing free outpatient services, medicines, and domiciliary visits to the poor.

The nineteenth century – epidemics, epidemiology, and the Medical Reform Act of 1858

The Industrial Revolution saw enormous increases in the population seeking work in factories. This in turn led to overcrowding, and the associated poor sanitation facilitated the rapid spread of epidemics such as cholera and tuberculosis. It was clear that poverty and ill health were closely interconnected and could no longer be neglected. Sickness spread rapidly from the poor to the affluent, and the illness and disability of the workforce significantly affected the productivity of businesses and factories. With this in mind, the voluntary hospitals received subscriptions from the gentry, civic worthies and industrialists, who would in turn sponsor the care of their workers in hospitals. Physicians and surgeons were not usually involved in the management of these hospitals (the preserve of the subscribers) but held honorary appointments, offering their services for free, ostensibly as an act of public service. These public acts of charity offered aspiring doctors access to powerful and wealthy patients, and also brought fees from medical school apprentices who would act as fee-paying assistants. During the course of the eighteenth and nineteenth centuries, the voluntary hospitals set up for the deserving poor helped advance the status, power and wealth of the medical profession.

In response to the multitude of charlatans and quacks claiming to be able to administer 'physic', the Medical Reform Act of 1858 (which brought into being the General Medical Council) created a single medical oversight body for the United Kingdom. Medical Practitioners on the Medical Register would henceforth only be licensed by the established corporations (Physicians, Surgeons, and Apothecaries) and Universities. Therefore all doctors would have the same legal (if not social) status, and doctors would be distanced from the quackery associated with herbalists, homeopaths and others. It also allowed doctors the right to self-regulate their profession. This self-regulation lasted until 2007 and the White Paper: *Trust, Assurance and Safety – The Regulation of Health Professionals in the 21st Century* (DH, 2007).

The nineteenth century also saw the establishment of Medical Societies and journals, such as *The Lancet* (1823), and the British Medical Association (1832). These helped elevate the status of the medical profession as both learned and respectable, and distinct from 'trade unions'. They also provided, and continue to provide, fora for debate about the development of medical practice and of the profession itself.

Poor relief

As the population of Britain expanded rapidly through the industrialisation and urbanisation of the nineteenth century, the numbers of paupers became a major concern to both doctors and the government. There was widespread concern that state-funded poor-relief was being abused by paupers, since poor-relief expenditure had increased from 1% of GDP in 1750 to 2.7% in 1821. Debates about the poor laws in the nineteenth century mirror many views of the critics of the NHS and welfare state today. The clergyman, political economist and demographer Thomas Malthus (1766–1834) argued that by supporting paupers, the Poor Law allowed the population in poverty to increase and that this in turn would have a severely negative impact on the working society which funded poor-relief. He felt that although the severe distress of a few would be worse without the poor laws, this would be outweighed by greater benefit across society as a whole. Malthus advocated workhouses for the poor rather than handouts.

There was also concern about the inequity and variation of poor law provision in different parishes, that poor law handouts were bringing down the wages of non-claimants and thereby reducing the motivation to work. These views, coupled with the Asian cholera epidemic of 1831–32, led the lawyer Edwin Chadwick (1800–1890) to believe that 'the greatest good for the greatest number' required government action. The response was the 1832 *Royal Commission into the operation of the Poor Laws*, and later in 1834 The *Poor Law Amendment Act*. This Act grouped together Parishes into Poor Law Unions under the auspices of a Board of Guardians. Workhouses would be built to separate the aged and infirm, children, able-bodied males, and able-bodied females. The Act abolished 'outdoor relief', so that no able-bodied people would have support unless they entered a workhouse, where conditions meant that only the most desperate would choose to become inmates. There was also a central authority, the Poor Law Commissioners, who would supervise the organisation and administration of relief in the Poor Law Unions.

The Poor Law Unions commissioned doctors to provide care to workhouse paupers, and (predictably) the cheapest tender was usually successful, leading to opposition from medical bodies. Similar tactics were used by the Friendly Societies, and in response doctors tried to organise themselves against their perceived inadequate remuneration. The establishment of both the British Medical Association (BMA) and the Medical Register were vital for doctors to raise themselves from being mere tradesmen competing for the cheapest contract to the status of an organised and professional body that enjoys widespread respect.

Leadership in nineteenth century medicine

It would be unfair to consider all nineteenth century British doctors as purely self-interested, seeking to elevate their status above that of tradesmen, doing charity work in order to earn the favour of rich patrons, and creating cartels to secure their income. In the main, doctors were already hard-working individuals committed to the care of their patients, often looking after charity cases for no return, and appalled by the living conditions of their pauper patients. This is exemplified by the work in London of two nineteenth-century medical leaders, Dr William Marsden and Dr John Simon.

William Marsden (1796–1867) was a Sheffield-born son of a victualler who turned down the opportunity for partnership in a drug business to train as a Surgeon at St Bartholomew's. In 1827, the year he joined the Royal College of Surgeons, he was appalled when he was unable to admit to hospital an 18-year-old girl he found dying on the steps of St Andrew's Church in Holborn. As she did not have a letter of sponsorship from a hospital governor or subscriber, she was refused hospital treatment. The following year Marsden set up a dispensary, 'The London General Institution for the Gratuitous Cure of Malignant Diseases', where the only criteria for admission were poverty and disease. This met with considerable opposition, but as the only London hospital admitting the poor without sponsors and also the only hospital which was prepared to admit cholera patients during the 1830s epidemics, a body of wealthy subscribers enabled Marsden to expand his hospital. With Queen Victoria's patronage, it became the Royal Free Hospital in 1837. Demand continued to grow, and by 1844 the hospital was treating 30,000 patients a year. Marsden became deeply affected by his wife's death from cancer in 1846 and established 'The Free Cancer Hospital' in 1851. This was eventually renamed the Royal Marsden in recognition of the vision and leadership of its founder.

John Simon (1816–1904) trained and worked as a surgeon at St Thomas', and became a Fellow of the Royal Society for his work on the thyroid gland at the age of 29. In 1847, he published a paper *On the aims and philosophic method of pathological research* which articulated the uncommon view that there would be a benefit to society through preventative medicine to help stem the tide of epidemics. After the limited effect of the 1834 Poor Law Amendment Act, the government response to the epidemics was the Public Health Act of 1848. This recommended that local authorities improve sanitation and established the General Board of Health. However, this Board had few powers and did little to improve sanitation (indeed, London was excluded due to prohibitive cost). Simon became the first Medical Officer of Health to London, the first time a doctor held a significant administrative position in public health. The Poor Law Boards of 1832 did not hold the view that medical men had a role to play in improving the health and sanitation of Britain's impoverished classes, and indeed the first General Board of Health created by the Public Health Act had no doctors, but rather two peers and a barrister.

Simon used his scientific expertise, powers of persuasion and leadership to expose and help improve the torrid state of London's poor. One example is in the registering of deaths. Simon realised that the efficacy of any interventions and of highlighting health problems lay with accurate and timely statistics of deaths within the city boundary. He appealed to the Registrar-General for help, and in turn, each of the nine city registrars provided the reports of the causes of deaths in their wards during the previous week for Simon to review. This prompt reporting allowed Simon to focus inspections and improvements where they were most needed. He established the Epidemiological Society of London in 1850 and in 1855 (along with abolishing cesspools) he was appointed to the new Board of Health which replaced the Poor Law Board of Health.

The government of the time had no statutory medical role other than during epidemics. This frustrated Simon, who had no wish 'To stand in the ante-chambers of legislation' awaiting implementation of sanitary reforms. Simon backed his arguments with compelling epidemiological evidence, such as the rates of cholera for different water-suppliers in London. Simon argued incessantly that a ministry of public health was essential, and in 1859 he was rewarded when the Board of Health became absorbed by the Privy Council, and Simon became Chief Medical Officer. He eventually resigned due to frustrations with government bureaucracy in 1867, but his work on sanitation made radical improvements to the health of Britain's cities, and became a model for public health provision around the world.

Medical advances, physical degeneration and the welfare state

The nineteenth century witnessed significant advances in pathological anatomy, microbiology, anaesthesia and antisepsis. For the first time, operations became relatively humane, and safer. The surgeon's status as the new hero of medicine was established in 1902 when Frederic Treves (1853–1923) safely operated on Edward VII's perforated appendix two days before the coronation. The king did not want surgery, but Treves successfully persuaded him, knowing that without surgery a funeral rather than a coronation would follow. Treves received a baronetcy, and the market for private surgery and the wealth of elite surgeons rapidly developed in London. By the turn of the century, the majority of doctors were making their living in general practice employed either by Friendly Societies paid for by working men or by Poor Law practices.

National concern about the state of the nation's health was prompted when recruitment for the Boer War (1899–1902) revealed a large proportion of potential recruits to be unfit. Together with concerns about socialism and borrowing from continental models of organising care, the government accepted that it would need to intervene in the welfare of the country's health. Lloyd George's subsequent welfare reforms introduced school medical inspections, state pensions and, in 1911, the National Insurance Act. This required a contribution from the employee, the employer and the state. In return, the employee (but not his family) would receive medical care and unemployment pay. General practitioners were resistant to becoming state employees, but compromised on being paid by the number of patients that they had on their books. This system covered about a third of the working population, who were predominantly manual labourers, as the higher-income and self-employed were excluded. This allowed general practitioners to maintain their independence and to gain supplementary income from the growing middle classes.

Doctors were consistently reluctant to be direct employees of the state, preferring to be contracted providers – something which has continued to be seen in subsequent generations (see Chapter 2). This desire for independence perhaps explains the mistrust and suspicion doctors have felt between themselves and the government bodies by whom they are paid and managed. The national insurance healthcare was administered via the Friendly Societies, industrial insurance companies and trade unions. This was, in essence, a public–private partnership.

Although seen by some as the foundation of the welfare state (and therefore as an act of great beneficence), since the elderly, women, children and the unemployed were excluded, it is also very possible to view the Liberal government's primary aim in 1911 as maintaining the country's workforce to help drive the Empire's economy. Workers also resented having to pay for drugs and hospital treatment, and there were serious concerns that firms would be less inclined to take on workers due to increased costs from employer contributions.

The extension of national insurance during the 1920s saw greater numbers of people covered so as to include widows, dependants and orphans. It also saw the closure of workhouses and the abolition of the poor law with poor law hospitals now being run by local government. National insurance helped place the family doctor in Britain as a valued and trusted member of the local community. By 1939, there were 18,000 general practitioners compared to only 2,800 hospital consultants. By contrast, other countries' health systems had much greater emphasis on specialists. For example, in the USA during the twentieth century general practice virtually disappeared in favour of patients seeing specialists from the outset (a trend the USA is now trying to reverse).

The 'Golden Age' of medicine

The great advance in pharmacology arose with the success of the 'sulpha' drugs of the 1930s in treating bacterial infection, and, after the Second World War, penicillin. This progress was also seen in diagnostics with the application of X-rays, electrocardiograms, blood and microbiological tests. The medical advances of the mid-twentieth century were seen as a golden age of therapeutic and diagnostic advance.

It also saw the nature of the doctor–patient relationship change. In the era before the doctor had access to much therapeutic power or technology to aid diagnosis, he relied heavily on being a friendly visiting physician, on the laying on of hands and on supporting the patient psychologically through illness. As diagnostic and therapeutic power to alter the course of disease developed, physicians' overall approach became more impersonal as they began to assess patients objectively in terms of test results, with a potential loss to the historic yet holistic and individual approach. This is perhaps part of the reason for the renaissance in popularity of alternative medicine, where paying clients receive a more personal treatment.

The advances of the twentieth century brought significant increases in the complexity and cost of healthcare. In 1900, a doctor could visit a patient alone, with his Gladstone bag containing all he might need (and all that he could offer); and a surgeon would often operate at a patient's own home. As the century progressed, home visits became rarer as primary and secondary care relied on more complex investigations and treatments spread across many different health professionals.

This increased complexity required greater levels of administration, from which most doctors distanced themselves. General practitioners consistently did not want to become state employees, and hospital consultants with their honorary appointments continued to rely on the influence and patronage of the hospital management committees. The establishment and development of the National Health Service in 1948, described in the following chapter, sees doctors developing much closer relationships and understanding of management, health policy and health politics.

This chapter, a whistlestop tour from Babylon to the first half of the 20th century just prior to the NHS's formation, has described the evolution of the role of the doctor's position in society, as well as in doctors' professional ability to exert influence over disease processes and to shape the systems through which healthcare is provided. The evolution of the role of the clinician continues today through the recognition and development of clinical leadership at the heart of the multidisciplinary context of the modern NHS.

References and further reading

Abel-Smith, B. (1964) *The Hospitals 1500–1848: a Study in Social Administration in England and Wales*. Heinemann, London.

Bynum, W. (1994) *Science and the Practice of Medicine in the Nineteenth Century*. Cambridge University Press, Cambridge.

Conrad, L. *et al.* (1995) *The Western Medical Tradition: 800 BC to AD 1800*. Cambridge University Press, Cambridge.

Department of Health (2007) *Trust, Assurance and Safety –The Regulation of Health Professionals in the 21st Century*. HMSO, London.

Hollingsworth *et al.* (1986) *A Political Economy of Medicine: Great Britain and the United States*. Johns Hopkins University Press, Baltimore.

Lambert, R. (1963) *Sir John Simon, 1806–1906 and English Social Administration*. London.

Lindert, P. (1998) Poor relief before the Welfare State: Britain versus the Continent, 1780–1880. *European Review of Economic History*, **2**, 101–40.

Lloyd, G. *et al.* (1983) *Hippocratic Writings*. Penguin Classics, London.

McKeown, T. (1979) *The Role of Medicine*. Blackwell, Oxford.

Porter, R. (1996) *The Cambridge Illustrated History of Medicine*. Cambridge University Press, Cambridge.

Sandwith, F. (1960) *Surgeon Compassionate: The Story of Dr William Marsden*. Peter Davies, London.

Shorter, E. (1991) *Doctors and their Patients*. Transaction Publishers, New Brunswick.

Stevens, R. (1966) *Medical Practice in Modern England: The Impact of Specialization and State Medicine*. Yale University Press, New Haven.

Wesley, J. (1747) *Primitive Physick: Or, an Easy and Natural Method of Curing Most Diseases.*

CHAPTER 2

A brief history of the NHS

Nemonique Sam and Benjamin M. Thomas

This chapter follows on from the history and context begun in the previous chapter. With the founding of the NHS, a new era began. Whilst the new era has brought enormous benefits to patients and clinicians alike, it has also meant challenges to clinical autonomy and put pressure on the interests of doctors versus the rest of society. This chapter explores the origins of the NHS, and the numerous waves of change that have subsequently occurred. It gives an overview of some of the political and organisational complexities of this extraordinary service. Many of the issues which we think of as peculiar to the modern NHS have actually existed in some form since the service's inception. An understanding of these will provide a comprehensive framework for the modern clinical leader in the NHS.

The birth of the NHS

Since 1948 the National Health Service has provided residents of the UK with comprehensive universal healthcare funded through central taxation and free at the point of delivery. It has evolved through six decades of significant social, technological and political change, and, as one of the largest sources of government expenditure, it is a consistently hot political topic.

The NHS has its origins in the Liberal social welfare agenda of the early twentieth century. As detailed in Chapter 1, healthcare in the UK prior to the NHS was not provided in a systematic or coherent way. It was provided by a medley of poorly coordinated providers consisting of voluntary organisations, municipal organisations, cottage-industry general practitioners, some funded by national insurance, others charging fees from certain members of society and providing to others for free.

By the 1930s it was clear that the health system in place was not viable, financially or politically. However, the Second World War interrupted discussion about the shape of a future national health service as the government was effectively forced to nationalise the hospital system in preparation for war casualties. The speed and efficiency with which this occurred demonstrated that it was possible for healthcare services to be transformed rapidly, and that administration and account-ability by central government was plausible. Translating war-time learning to a sustainable post-war system was not a simple process since various stakeholders, including the medical profession, believed they stood to lose from a state-control-led nationalised system and were therefore resistant to change.

In 1942, William Beveridge produced a seminal report about social secur-ity, in which he made reference to an assumption that everyone would be enti-tled to comprehensive healthcare. This sparked negotiations within the coali-tion government of the time, culminating in the White Paper of 1944.

The end of the war brought with it a Labour landslide victory and a health min-ister who has become famous as being the 'father of the NHS' – Aneurin Bevan. He was a charismatic leader who believed in the ideals of a national health service and built on the proposals outlined in the 1944 White Paper. He proposed a health-care service enacted in the 1946 Act that was centralised but administered locally by regional boards and district committees, which would provide comprehensive, universal, free healthcare, funded through general taxation. Bevan gave conces-sions to hospital doctors represented by the Royal Colleges – for example, allow-ing the independent governance of teaching hospitals, allowing private practice in hospital pay-beds and permitting doctors to sit on the new regional boards and district committees and to be paid merit awards in return for practising for the state. These concessions brought hospital doctors alongside government plans and were a politically astute way of splitting the medical profession between consult-ants and GPs, who were represented by the British Medical Association (BMA). The GPs were also granted concessions – in some ways greater ones: they did not become employees of the state as Bevan wanted, but rather continued to receive 'capitation' payments and to maintain independent contractor status. The argu-ment over GP pay continued until the very last moment before the service was born in 1948, and it remains a clear demonstration to every government and health minister since then of the power that the medical profession wields in shaping the NHS. Other clinical workers, including nurses, did not have representation with the government during this period in which the arrangements were being put into place for the birth of the NHS.

The first 10 years

The NHS was brought into being on 5 July 1948. Providing healthcare free at the point of delivery was, as might be expected, extremely popular both amongst the public and amongst the medical profession.

The vision was to amalgamate previously disparate groups of services rang-ing from mental healthcare to routine dental care. The underlying financial methodology of the early NHS was for funding to be raised entirely through taxation with no charges levied to the consumer at the point of use. Bevan shrewdly recognised early on that '...expectation will always exceed capacity'. The advantages to funding from central taxation were simplicity, cost-effect-iveness (very low administration costs) and the progressive nature of funding (the rich subsidising the poor through paying more tax). The NHS's current financial structure remains very close to this, despite numerous reviews. No government review to date has identified an effective or politically acceptable alternative to central taxation.

Some policymakers initially calculated – erroneously – that improving health would reduce demand on the service. Equally, many clinicians thought that, free from any financial constraint arising from the patient's ability to pay, they would be able to deliver the most effective treatment without having to consider costs. Needless to say, spending on the NHS grew rapidly during the early years, far exceeding initial estimates.

The NHS was in direct competition for resources with other government departments, such as education and housing. The Treasury had a significant role to play in determining the levels of funding and ultimately the evolution of the service. The prescription charge was introduced in 1949, followed in 1951 by charges for dental and optical services, aimed at capping NHS spending at £400 million. The NHS probably required far more than this figure to deliver the services that the nation required, but this arbitrary artificial ceiling of £400 million imposed in the early history of the NHS was used as a benchmark to justify government spending for years thereafter. A significant consequence of this was a focus on running the service rather than on investment in the service, particularly in capital projects.

The first NHS review was undertaken in 1953, when the Guillebaud Com-mittee was commissioned to make an assessment of funding within the service. Three years later it reported back, stating first that there were no opportunities for new income sources beyond taxation, and second that cost reduction was not likely to be possible, and might indeed rise. Third, the committee found that capital expenditure was too low.

Public expectations continually rise regarding what the NHS is able to deliver. The post-war era heralded a new age for the use of technology in medicine, which has continued to the present at an ever-increasing rate, further driving up costs. Unlike other industries where technological advances tend to reduce cost, in medicine technology generally leads to more expenditure, not less. Examples of innovation during the early years of the NHS include the widespread use of antibiotics, the routine use of diagnostic investigations such as radiography and pathological analysis, and electrocardiography – all of which are now taken for granted as essential to the modern health service.

During the 1950s, services began to need to be rationed in some way. Central government imposed capped budgets on local authorities, which became a guiding principle of the NHS. This allowed local authorities a degree of relative autonomy within fixed financial boundaries, meaning that a range of ways of providing healthcare were acceptable. In principle, central government aimed to set the over-arching aims and direction, which then passed through regional health boards that oversaw implementation at a local level by GPs or hospitals. This system remains to the present day, although the hierarchical structure with central government at the top remains a source of tension with local deliverers of healthcare.

The tension between central government and front-line clinicians is partly due to the lines of financial accountability that central taxation implies. The Minister of Health has overall financial accountability for the NHS, whilst individual spending decisions were effectively devolved to local clinicians' professional judgement. Capped budgets from the Treasury during the 1950s placed the Minister in a difficult position with NHS staff as he was unable to increase finances and struggled to persuade front-line staff to implement national policy. This was an early manifestation of an ongoing problem of how to balance professional autonomy with political control and a fixed budget. This is particularly true for general practice which has always maintained its independent contractor status, and ultimately has the ability to cripple NHS budgets through its role as a gatekeeper to prescriptions and hospital referrals. In the 1950s, the medical profession was represented at every level of the NHS structure through medical advisory committees. One notable effect of this representation was persistent maintenance of the status quo whenever government policy implementation was attempted. Unfortunately, this resistance to change is a feature that doctors have consistently demonstrated as a professional group throughout the history of the NHS.

The emerging management culture

The first decade of the NHS was essentially a time of consolidation for the new and innovative service, constrained within financial limits with limited overall change from its inception. The 1960s signalled an end to post-war stagnation. Growth, innovation and expansion were key themes for both of the main political parties trying to outdo each other in their 1959 pre-election manifestos with promises of greater resources, more staff and better services for the NHS.

There was a rapid growth in public expenditure from 1960–75. Spending on healthcare as a share of GDP rose from 3.5% to 5.6%, with the greatest increase in expenditure between 1970 and 1974. Comparatively, other Western countries were also spending more on health, in many cases outstripping UK spending. A new concept of sustainable planning in government emerged, embodied by the creation of the Public Expenditure Survey Committee (PESC) in 1961, which aimed to control all public spending and heralded the arrival of cost–benefit analyses by all government departments, including health. This represented the arrival of management efficiency as a concept and also saw the emergence in the UK of health economics as an academic and policy discipline. In order to service the new requirements of organisational assessment and change, a new cadre of expert administrators and managers appeared, often from disciplines unrelated to health, such as retail or industry.

By the 1960s, the health service was widely recognised as a major achievement, both politically and socially, and as indispensable. Equally, however, there were major resourcing and equity issues. Health economists provided evidence that the health needs of individuals needed to be weighed against the wider healthcare needs of the population with a sense of equity. There was a realisation that massive cash injections would be required to fund a population health system and that the NHS had a duty to ration resources between the needs of the individual and the needs of the population. In 1962, the first comprehensive review of the NHS was carried out by Enoch Powell, the then Health Minister, entitled *A Hospital Plan for England and Wales* (Ministry of Health, 1962). This sought to create a system of hospitals that would be matched to population needs, rather than the inherited systems which concentrated provision near metropolitan centres where specialists had previously stood to gain most by private practice. Under Powell's plan, each area of the country would have had a 600–800 bed district general hospital serving 100,000 to 150,000 people with a drive to nationalise structures and standards. This nationalisation of standards is a recurrent theme throughout NHS history, one which is played out in the modern NHS under various guises and institutions, but which began in the 1960s as a scrutiny of variation.

Concurrently, General Practice established with the government a charter which changed GP pay, and provided financial incentives for practice development. The other main reviews of the decade assessed aspects that the NHS continues to address today: firstly the Porritt report (1962) made recommendations to address the separate nature of the tripartite service and to integrate what was to become primary and secondary care. Subsequently, the separate Cogwheel and Salmon reports (both in 1967) advocated increased involvement of clinicians in management roles.

A further theme of NHS history is its politicisation and coupling with the political cycle, which may explain the spending cuts for capital investment over time. Given the relatively short cycle of government compared with the many years taken to plan, design and build a new hospital, successive administrations realised that any plans which were approved would only come to fruition after the next election. There was therefore no political imperative to win votes in this way in comparison to short-term fixes.

It was also clear that the existing separate administration of hospital services, primary care services and local authority services was illogical and that a single authority responsible for all these services would be a far superior solution. Area Health Authorities (AHA) were proposed with shared geographical local and health authority boundaries and a reduced number of executive boards, giving better management and greater power towards long-term planning. Regional executive agencies were designed to sit between government and the new AHAs. A new introduction to the mix was the Community Health Council (CHC) giving voice to patients at an area level alongside each AHA. GPs remained outside of this system. As independent contractors to the NHS, they would handle their own administration through Family Practice Committees (FPCs) aligned to each AHA.

During this shift to a more managerial culture, criticism was voiced in the House of Commons over the increased layering of bureaucracy at every level within the NHS and of managers taking over the running of the ship. The number of administrative and clerical staff rose from 87,000 in 1973 to 113,000 in 1976 as central government increasingly tried to exercise control over the activity of local health providers in the new health economy.

The Resource Allocation Working Party (RAWP) was established in 1976 in an attempt to allocate resources more fairly according to need. For the first time that were weighted towards factors of standardised mortality and age, demonstrating an understanding of significant national variation and shortcomings in existing services. However, recession and inflation during the 1970s meant that NHS funding was squeezed hard, with overall annual increases in income but larger annual increases in spending due to the running costs of new hospitals combined with wider social changes.

In 1973, a strike by ancillary workers demonstrated that the NHS was not immune to trade union action. The professional bodies also developed trade union tactics as they competed for an increase in wages. In October 1975, junior doctors withdrew labour over pay, leading to a system of pay according to 'overtime' above a standard working week of 40 hours. Simultaneously, a plethora of patients' associations, pressure groups and charitable campaigning organisations were born which have subsequently become core to the health policy framework. The demands on the NHS were rapidly increasing, with groups calling for the NHS to provide extra services for their members, ranging from mental health services to renal dialysis and better access in general.

The 'Capitalist NHS'

Margaret Thatcher came to power in 1979 with a clear market-orientated approach to running the NHS. During her leadership, Britain continued to have a troubled economy with rising public spending. With an increasingly service-oriented economy and the beginning of an information era of mass telecommunications, consumerism and market forces drove the privatisation of industry.

In 1982, a leaked cabinet paper showed the government had discussed plans to privatise the NHS and replace the system of central taxation with a personal insurance system. The plans died quickly amidst a political storm, but suspicion about the long term plans of the Conservatives for the NHS remained. In 1982, the reorganisation that took place was a simplification, with the AHAs swept away and the smaller districts becoming the unit of healthcare provision in the form of district health authorities (DHAs) encouraging local decision-making. Local district general hospitals were limited in size to serve the local community and local authorities were no longer co-located with the providers of healthcare. GPs continued to remain outside the system as independent providers.

During a time of economic instability and overall falls in NHS income in real terms, the government needed to improve efficiency in public services and started to focus on performance indicators. In this way, accountability could be demonstrated to ministers as well as to the public (since the results were published). This enabled policymakers to ask questions of providers in order to compare differences, as well as to allow a more detailed dissection by ministers who could use performance indicators to influence policy changes. The original performance indicators for healthcare measured activity rather than outcomes, without specifically looking at quality.

In 1983 the managing director of Sainsbury's, Roy Griffiths, published a report which suggested implementing a more managerial structure tasked with making change happen in NHS. The report proposed a management board at the top, with the secretary of state as Chair and a Chief Executive for the NHS, followed by general managers for each region, district and unit. Managers were to be recruited from any sector, and paid according to performance. These changes heralded an era of assertive management imposing authority over the medical profession. In this system, as with all systems of NHS governance to date, the political weight at the top of the structure remained as centralised control.

Margaret Thatcher believed that the GP gatekeepers to the NHS held the key to controlling healthcare costs. With a growing elderly population and increasingly expensive technologies, the emphasis on preventative medicine became attractive in order to reduce hospital admissions and prescriptions.

Although spending on primary care increased and the number of family doctors rose, no real savings were made in terms of prescribing or referrals. Subsequently, in 1984, the health minister Kenneth Clarke announced a 'limited list' of drugs in order to try to control NHS drug budgets in primary care. In 1987 a White Paper called *Promoting Better Health* was produced which strengthened the Family Practice Committees (FPCs) in exercising management control over GPs in terms of cost-effectiveness, performance and quality. Disease prevention targets were set, together with surveys of customer satisfaction, and monitoring of prescribing and referral patterns. Financial incentives were introduced for GPs to improve health through vaccinations and other approaches to preventative medicine and health promotion.

Reorganisation continued with the perceived failures of earlier attempts being blamed upon over-complexity and blanket policy. General management practices were recommended, encouraging clear leadership, flexibility and teamwork. Concepts of audit and improved healthcare informatics were introduced, as were indicators of performance. The 1989 White Paper, *Working for Patients*, was published in response to the perceived hospital monopoly over community care and increased waiting lists, aiming to reallocate power to those using the services as opposed to those providing them. The Conservative government went on to implement the proposals laid out in this document and in the 1990 *NHS and Community Care Act*. The concept of competition was introduced, challenging the vertical flow of funds and bringing with it the greatest administrative change in the history of the NHS.

The purchaser–provider divide

Despite increased spending, with more doctors and nurses, public opinion was against the Conservative government's management of the health service. Attempts to boost efficiency were interpreted as underfunding. The lack of data made measuring efficiency difficult, but stories of closed wards and doctors being unable to treat patients were prominent in the media.

The 1989 review led to every aspect of the NHS being examined including the fundamental ideology of funding through central taxation. The most significant change to the NHS as a result of this was the split between the purchasers of healthcare – the health authorities – and the providers of healthcare – the hospital and community trusts. Health authorities would have the ability to make efficiencies through competitive purchasing. This would create a market within which a plurality of competing providers would look for business. An extension of this pseudo-market was the creation of GP 'fundholders' who would manage their own budgets and purchase care on behalf of their patients.

Private providers were given considerably greater and more direct access to bid for services from purchasers, which remains a subject of great controversy. The running of these new trusts meant that the managerial culture of the NHS was strengthened with the creation of new boards, composed of non-executives and executive officers.

The move to 'market medicine' provoked strong criticism, including from the British Medical Association, which unpicked the policy and instigated a concerted marketing campaign against the proposals. This was a big shift in the fundamental make-up of the NHS and firmly placed market-driven ideology within a fundamentally socialist welfare system. Concerns were raised about creating a competitive market setting, and dividing the delivery of healthcare, as well as about the potentially perverse incentives of fundholding where GPs could make cost savings for personal gain by limiting expensive treatments. There was further argument that creating a managerial market culture would lead to a service loaded with uncaring bureaucracy.

In the creation of this new policy, Margaret Thatcher largely excluded the medical profession from discussions, in part because doctors were seen more as part of the problem rather than part of the solution. In 1990, the new GP contract defined in relatively high detail the services that GPs were expected to provide, and encouraged the public to think of themselves as consumers of healthcare. As part of the move to the new market approach, the clinically led FPCs were replaced by managerially led Family Health Services Authorities (FHSAs). Although there was significant opposition to the contract itself, GP salaries rose significantly as a result.

The National Health Service and Community Care Act was passed in 1990 with little reference or concession to the detractors. In the absence of pilot studies and evaluation, national policy was enforced. By the mid-1990s, the market was established with purchasers and providers. However, in several areas there was little competition between providers, with London and some cities being the exceptions. The purchaser became re-branded as the 'commissioner', reflecting the scenario that purchasers and providers were often locked in a mutual arrangement that needed shaping by one side, and that the purchaser had the power to shape future provider services. For example, compared to the rest of the UK, London hospitals had historically been overfunded such that previously outlying areas had to send their patients into the city to access services. Commissioning allowed this to be rebalanced by facilitating the access of services closer to home.

The new market-driven NHS was expensive to run and required many more layers of managers at all levels in the organisation. The NHS Management Executive was introduced at the centre, in the Department of Health (DH), and previous regional health authorities were merged into eight regional NHS Management Executives. External management consultants were employed with increasing frequency to implement reforms such as new information technology.

Fundholding for GPs enabled GPs to use their funds to create new services for their patients and buy fast-track access to hospitals. This was an illustration of the power of GPs to shape local services, and an instigator towards a drive for a 'primary care led' NHS. GPs began to form groups and consortia to manage purchasing over a wider area, which began to shift the balance of power from secondary to primary care.

This chapter has built on the historical context from Chapter 1 to explore the creation and early years of the NHS through to the most recent reforms of the current Labour government. Common themes emerge about financial constraints, political involvement, and the role of the doctor in shaping (or resisting) health system change. Greater familiarity with NHS's history and evolution is a useful context in which to consider the NHS today and to look ahead to future challenges.

References and further reading

Beveridge, W. (1942) *Social Insurance and Allied Services*. HMSO, London.

Committee of Enquiry into the Cost of the National Health Service (1956) *Report of the Committee of Enquiry into the Cost of the National Health Service (Guillebaud report)* HMSO, London.

Darzi, A. (2008) *High Quality Care for All: NHS Next Stage Review Final Report*. Department of Health, London.

Department of Health (1987) *Promoting Better Health: the Government's Programme for Improving Primary Health Care*. HMSO, London.

Department of Health (1989) *Working for Patients*. HMSO, London.

Department of Health (1997) *The new NHS: Modern, Dependable*. Stationery Office, London.

Department of Health (2000) *The NHS Plan: a plan for investment, a plan for reform*. Stationery Office, London.

Griffiths, R. (1983) *NHS Management Inquiry: Report to the Secretary of State for Social Services*. DHSS, London.

Hansard (1971) *House of Commons Debates*. **820**: col 611 (1 Jul 71).

Hansard (1973) *House of Commons Debates*. **853**: col 86 (27 Mar 73).

Jones, C. (1950) *Cabinet Committee on the National Health Service: Enquiry into the financial working of the service*. Public Records Office, London.

Klein, R. (2006) *The New Politics of the NHS: from Creation to Reinvention*, 5th edn. Radcliffe Publishing, Oxford.

Ministry of Health, Department of Health for Scotland (1944) *A National Health Service*. HMSO, London.

Ministry of Health (1962) *A Hospital Plan for England and Wales*. HMSO, London.

Resource Allocation Working Party (1976) *Sharing Resources for Health in England: Report of the Resource Allocation Working Party*. HMSO, London.

Rivett, G. C. (1998) *From Cradle to Grave: Fifty Years of the NHS*. King's Fund, London.

Rivett, G. C. (2009) *National Health Service History*. http://www.nhshistory.net/ (accessed 1 July 2009).

Royal Commission on the National Health Service (1979) *Report of the Royal Commission*. HMSO, London.

Webster, C. (2002) *The National Health Service: a Political History*, 2nd edn. Oxford University Press, Oxford.

CHAPTER 3

The present NHS

Erik Mayer, Benjamin Thomas and Paul Corrigan

In recent years, as devolved governments have become established in Scotland, Wales and Northern Ireland, the picture of the 'NHS' in the UK's constituent countries has diverged. This chapter focuses on the reforms of the Labour government since 1997, focusing on NHS England. The English NHS stands out as having introduced an activity-based payment system, a payer–provider split (as described in Chapter 2) and as having diversified the supply of the provision of care. The other countries have pursued less radical paths. Time will tell which approach is most successful. The divergence of the various countries' NHSs can be regarded as a large natural experiment in how to design and run a universal health service paid for out of central taxation providing equal access for all free at the point of need.

When Labour came to government in 1997 there was a general sense, not confined to the left of the political spectrum, that the NHS was under-funded. The most important consequence of this was difficulties in accessing care: waits of twelve or more hours in A&E were not uncommon; nor were waits for elective surgery of over a year, sometimes two. When budgets came under pressure, or when there was a surge in demand for the system (for example, in winter 'flu crises), attention would turn to dealing with the acutely unwell, and elective activity often ground to a halt.

For many years, funding to the NHS as a percentage of national wealth (GDP) had lagged behind the European average. The Wanless report (2002) outlined three future scenarios for NHS funding and spending levels, all of which required substantial funding increases. In 2001, the Prime Minister Tony Blair made a highly publicised pledge to increase NHS funding to the European average by 2005. This chapter discusses the performance improvements expected in return and the policy levers used to drive health reform.

In economic terms, the reforms have focused on creating better value (through more patient and population benefit) in both the demand side and the supply side of healthcare. On the demand side, as described in Chapter 2, Strategic Health Authorities and Primary Care Trusts commission (buy) healthcare which fits local needs and regional strategies. On the supply side (provision of care, both in the community and hospital-based), a series of measures including targets, patient choice, diversifying supply and including private- and voluntary-sector providers all aim to put performance pressure on the NHS. Supply and demand are linked by a payment system in which hospitals are paid for activity: Payment by Results or PbR.

Regional management and commissioning

The separation of those buying care from those providing it is the cornerstone of recent NHS reform. This division aims to minimise the conflicts of interest and maximise the pressure that can be put on suppliers to deliver high-quality care relevant to the needs of the local population. It allows each organisation to 'specialise' and become expert in its core function.

As described in Chapter 2, NHS England is currently divided into ten regions or Strategic Health Authorities (SHAs), each with its own Chief Executive, Chair and Board, reporting to the NHS Chief Executive in the Department of Health (DH). Each of the ten is required to develop and deliver a regional health strategy and a strategy for the NHS workforce (both clinical and non-clinical), and its performance is managed by the DH.

In turn, the ten SHAs are the line management for 152 Primary Care Trusts (PCTs). The key role of the PCT is to commission (buy) care on behalf of the population living within its geographic boundaries. Eighty per cent of NHS funds flows through SHAs to PCTs. The money given to each PCT is calculated using a weighted capitation formula. This means that a specific amount is allocated for every person living within the boundary of the PCT each year. The precise sum varies by means of complex formulae that take into account aspects of different parts of the population and their deprivation and their propensity to illness. The more challenged areas get greater per capita funding.

Each PCT has a Chief Executive, a Chair and a Board. Most PCTs evolved out of parts of the NHS which previously provided community care. Now, as commissioners, PCTs are expected to commission community as well as hospital-based care, so they are in the process of divesting (shedding) their community provider activities. This enables them both to resolve potential conflicts of interest and to devote more attention to commissioning.

Since PCTs are relatively new organisations, and since commissioning is also relatively novel for the NHS, a major system challenge for the system is developing PCTs' capabilities to be effective commissioners. One of the main requirements for a PCT is to develop a five-year Commissioning Strategy Plan. This outlines the way in which the PCT plans to improve the health and healthcare of its local population. This process starts with an understanding of the population. Every PCT needs to carry out a Joint Strategic Needs Assessment (JSNA) with its local authority. This legal requirement demonstrates how the local authority and the PCT jointly understand what the health and the healthcare needs of their local population are and demonstrates how they are going to work together to improve their health and healthcare provision. At present, too many PCTs view their main role as passing the money that they receive from the DH on to the local NHS hospital without changing the way in which health and healthcare is provided for their local population.

Commissioning is tightly linked to local primary care. Practice-based commissioners (PBC) are GPs and others who work closely with PCTs, enabling front-line clinicians to become more involved in commissioning decisions. The idea behind PBC is to place the day-to-day commissioning decisions in the hands of groups of GPs who make the key clinical decisions.

In 2007/08, a major new programme was introduced to both assess and develop PCTs as commissioning organisations. 'World Class Commissioning' (WCC) is an annual assurance programme that was introduced to assess how well each PCT was executing its commissioning responsibilities against a set of competencies, with criteria around their governance and outcome. The Department of Health has encapsulated its vision for WCC in the catchphrase 'Adding life to years and years to life'. A broad definition of commissioning is 'local investment to achieve the greatest health gain and to reduce health inequalities, at the best value'. Health economic evaluation of interventions, using QALYs (Quality Adjusted Life Years) to measure benefit is at the heart of WCC. The eleven competencies in the WCC framework are shown in Box 3.1. WCC dominates how Primary Care Trusts currently approach their strategy, development and healthcare purchasing activities.

Box 3.1 Eleven competencies for World Class Commissioning

1. Locally lead the NHS
2. Work with community partners
3. Engage with public and patients
4. Collaborate with clinicians
5. Manage knowledge and assess needs
6. Prioritise investment
7. Stimulate the market
8. Promote improvement and innovation
9. Secure procurement skills
10. Manage the local health system
11. Make sound financial investments

In February 2009 every PCT was given its first overall WCC score. The median score was between 'weak' and 'adequate' on most of the above eleven dimensions. The assessment will be repeated in 2010 and every year thereafter to monitor improvement. WCC sets a more formalised structure for embedding clinicians in healthcare purchasing decisions. The WCC framework formally recognises the value that clinicians bring to healthcare purchasing activity. World Class Commissioning competency No. 4 requires that commissioners should lead continuous and meaningful engagement with clinicians to inform strategy and drive quality, service design and resource utilisation. The expectation is that this involvement will come from a broad range of clinicians, including GPs, hospital doctors and non-medical clinicians.

As with any purchasing decision, to do it well you need to understand what you need to buy and what represents good value. Clinical expertise, therefore, is recognised as a core component of healthcare commissioning. For example, for understanding how to weight QALYs or how changes in clinical practice and technology may influence provision in the future, or for negotiating effectively with local providers, clinical skills (and credibility) are vital. These have been in short supply in most PCTs, many of which have not had medical or nursing directors. There remains an urgent need for clinical leadership particularly in PCTs, as well as in the more traditional domains of hospitals and other provider organisations; this is already creating opportunities for clinical leaders in a relatively new area for the NHS.

Measures to improve the performance of providers

Reform has also centred on measures to improve providers' performance. First, a set of national standards and national bodies has been established; second a new payment system has been introduced for hospitals which makes payments based on the amount of work done; and third a series of measures has been developed to introduce choice for patients about where to be treated and to make available non-NHS providers under the NHS umbrella. Finally, through Foundation Trusts, hospitals with increased freedoms and greater local accountability have been established under an independent regulator to encourage innovation. We will now consider each of these measures in turn.

A: National standards and national bodies

Whilst disparities remain between the different parts of the country, the last ten years has seen considerable strengthening of the national framework of institutions and aims within which the NHS operates. The most important of these have been national service frameworks in the most important disease areas, national quality regulation and inspection, NICE and national targets. Each of these is now considered.

(i) National Service Frameworks (NSFs)

The development of national standards for the major killers such as cancer and heart disease has had a direct effect upon disseminating best practice and reducing mortality. Before the introduction of national frameworks, the way in which a heart attack was dealt with in one part of the country was frequently different from treatment in a different region. The National Frameworks, developed primarily by clinicians under the leadership of a National Clinical Director (or 'Czar') demonstrate how good practice can be effectively developed, disseminated and implemented. The NSFs are backed up by a range of education and training packages designed to facilitate multidisciplinary provider learning from best practice, and which have proved fruitful in developing national approaches to healthcare, including an emphasis on prevention and detection, multidisciplinary collaboration and teamworking (see Chapter 4) and the creation of clinical networks on a regional basis.

(ii) Regulation and Inspection of Quality

In 1997, there was no national independent inspection of healthcare in the UK. These functions had existed for over 100 years in education and nearly 50 years in social care, but healthcare did not have its national equivalent to Her Majesty's Inspectorate (in education) or to the Social Services Inspectorate (in social services). In so far as they existed at all, this role was carried out within various specialties by the respective Royal Colleges. Over the last ten years, there have been several incarnations of the independent inspectorate, most recently the creation of the Care Quality Commission (CQC) in April 2009, a single organisation covering the inspection and regulation of both social care and healthcare.

(iii) NICE: The National Institute for Health and Clinical Excellence

Even more significant was the creation of an independent organisation to decide which drugs and technologies should be used within the NHS. NICE provides guidance regarding, for example, the funding of new and costly drugs. These are emotive and difficult decisions, which are often controversial, especially where end-of-life care is concerned. However, all health systems face such spending choices and constraints, and NICE, for all its drawbacks, has become something of a model for how to make cost-effectiveness decisions. A high proportion of hits to the NICE website come from overseas and a number of other countries have either set up analogous bodies, modelled on NICE, or use NICE guidance to inform their own country choices.

(iv) National targets

Faced with overflowing A&E Departments and waits of months or often years for elective procedures, the Labour government focused attention on access with the introduction of the 'four hour' target and the six-month elective access target, now at 18 weeks. Equal emphasis has been placed on specific areas of public concern in safety, most notably relating to MRSA (methicillin-resistant *Staphylococcus aureus*) infections. The high emphasis on these targets has led to improvement across the board in performance against them and subsequently very few patients now wait more than 18 weeks for elective procedures and breaches of the 'four hour' A&E wait in most parts of the country are rare. However, the 'performance function' required by a health service is much more complex and subtle than can be captured via access and infection targets. Clinicians and others have (with justification) complained that targets over-emphasise certain aspects of care at the expense of others which also matter to patients – clinical quality considered more broadly than just infection as an example. There has undoubtedly been 'gaming' behaviour designed to meet targets while failing to meet the spirit of performance the targets aim to foster. An example of this is admitting patients directly to a ward to avoid breaching the four-hour limit is an example. Another example from primary care has been preventing patients from scheduling advance appointments in order to comply with a 48 hour target to get a GP appointment.

The role of clinical leadership is both to help organisations deliver against government targets and also to act as a check against this type of gaming. More importantly, by having clinicians at the centre of how care is designed and organised and to have them working alongside managerial professionals, organisations should (in most cases) be able to easily meet targets and deliver performance well beyond them. National targets necessarily represent minimum standards. Clinical leadership can take an organisation way beyond compliance with that.

B: Payment for hospitals based on units of activity

In the past, the way in which the money flowed around the NHS was opaque. Some was given out locally through health boards and more was given out nationally through the Department of Health. One of the more alarming parts of the economics of this was that historically, if a hospital ran out of money in February, then it usually received more to see it through the financial year. The incentive system advocated spending more and doing little. Funding historically gave lump sums to providers based on an increment over the previous year's payment; the number of patients treated, and for what, was not significantly related to the sum received.

'Payment by Results' (PbR) has dramatically altered this disjunction between funding and patient care. It was introduced in 2002, when the Department of Health published *Reforming NHS Financial Flows: Introducing Payment by Results* (Department of Health, 2002). Classifying and coding healthcare provision is now essential, since the funds a provider receives is based on the type and number of cases handled. The essential component of PbR is the nationally agreed tariff for specific services – each intervention has a national price (adjusted regionally by the cost of doing business in different parts of England). There is ongoing debate about what the tariff should be for any particular procedure, but initially pricing was set by finding the average for particular procedures across hospitals. For example, the price of a hip replacement was the average cost to hospitals across the country, meaning that 50% of the hospitals were able to carry out the procedure for slightly less than the price and about 50% were carrying it out for more. The former group were able to make a surplus for each procedure and the latter made a loss. If the latter group failed to address its excess costs, it would lose more money the more patients it treated. Combining targets with activity-based payment creates powerful incentives for efficiency. Each year, the policy aim is to lower the tariff, both as average costs come down through hospitals finding more efficient ways to organise care, and by setting the tariff not at average cost but lower than that.

Currently, 'PbR' is something of a misnomer; it implies something about quality, but rather it represents payment for activity. More recently, PCTs have been introducing quality incentives for secondary care (so-called CQUINs – Commissioning for Quality and Innovation) which are a step towards making PbR worthy of the name.

C: Plurality of provision and patient choice

Many commentators believe patient choice is a new trend for the NHS. In fact, choice was in the NHS from its inception in 1948, when a leaflet went through everyone's door saying 'First choose your doctor'. This right to choose your GP has endured, although getting on (and off) GPs' lists has often been easier said than done.

More recent reforms on choice are focused at secondary care, enabling choice regarding which hospital you go to and when you want your procedures. Choice was initially offered as a choice between five providers, including where possible an independent sector provider, which could be a for-profit provider or a third-sector (charity or social) provider. Now, at least in theory, if a GP decides referral is needed, patients are able to choose to be treated at any provider in England that supplies services at tariff.

As an important influence on patient flows and volume, choice has the potential to have a huge impact on providers, which are now competing with each other for the patient, sometimes with the independent sector. Together with PbR, choice is a powerful lever to put pressure on NHS providers to up their game. If patients are truly deciding where to be treated, choice has the potential to reward those hospitals that provide care that patients find most agreeable.

Clearly, choice is only as good as the information informing choice. Various measures have been introduced to help referring clinicians and patients make more informed choices. Similarly, the IT infrastructure to implement choice has been a huge logistical effort, fraught with delays and problems. Since 2004, the 'Choose and Book' system has been progressively rolled out. It aims to connect secondary care appointment systems with primary care as well as providing basic information on choices available (NHS Connecting for Health, 2009).

D: Foundation hospitals: increased freedoms and greater local accountability

Although the majority of healthcare in the NHS takes place in primary care, hospitals continue to be the main public image of healthcare providers. The image of the hospital with its urgency and life or death choices plays strongly with the public. Foundation Trusts (FTs) are another pillar of reform designed to bring performance 'edge' to NHS providers and to create incentives for hospitals to up their game.

The first wave of ten Foundation Trusts (FT) were established in June 2004 and as of 1 June 2009, 121 were in operation across acute care and mental health. The basic thrust of FT policy is that, in return for demonstrating stable finances (and, increasingly, high and improving quality), a hospital's leadership receives greater freedom to be self-governing and to generate a financial surplus which is not clawed back by the system at the end of each year. They can also borrow and have access to a range of other funding streams.

Foundation Trusts are independent, not-for-profit organisations accountable to the local community and created with the purpose of increasing local autonomy, governance and accountability. This freedom and accountability aims to encourage local initiative and entrepreneurialism. FTs are first account-able to their own Boards of Directors, then accountable to their Governors and members (representatives of the local population). They are authorised and regulated by Monitor, the independent regulator of FTs. Traditionally, hos-pitals have been being accountable to the DH and the Secretary of State via the SHA (or previously Regional Health Authority). It is worth noting that an additional benefit of FT policy is to free the DH in general and the Secretary of State in particular from being held 'line accountable' for any failure in a provider, wherever it might be. By making local boards accountable, and seen to be accountable, the willingness of the DH and Ministers to devolve deci-sion-making power to the NHS is increased.

In order to become a Foundation Trust, the applying trust undergoes a three-phase process. Firstly there is a Strategic Health Authority-led phase, which prepares the NHS trust for the application process. Secondly, the Sec-retary of State phase determines whether applicant trusts are eligible to apply to Monitor for assessment. Finally, Monitor itself decides whether to authorise Foundation status. Monitor (2008b) fundamentally undertakes a risk assess-ment, looking for a robust, financially sound organisation, which is locally representative.

Current Government policy is that all mental health and acute trusts should become Foundation Trusts. However, it is likely that some trusts (possibly 20–30 of them), for various structural and operational reasons, will never be capable of breaking even or running their own organisation. Some of these trusts could become viable through mergers and takeovers, neither of which are straightforward options.

The 'Darzi Report': *High Quality Care for All* – and a look to the future

The structure and operation of the NHS described above, and the recent reforms outlined, have all been designed to improve the performance of the system. All provide opportunities for clinicians to contribute to making policy decisions more clinically informed, or to enable the effective implementation of policy locally. All, in short, call for clinical leadership.

Yet even more recently, the emphasis on clinical leadership has increased further. We are in an age of clinical leadership, including (until summer 2009) a surgeon health minister, Lord Darzi, who wrote the Foreword for this book. Darzi has spearheaded some of the most recent recommendations and changes. His report *High Quality Care for All* (timed to coincide with the NHS's 60th birthday in July 2008) represents an attempt to define the direction of the NHS over the next 5–10 years and beyond. Central to this is clinical quality and clinical leadership; both have greater emphasis now than at any stage in the NHS's history.

The report, based on the work of a number of clinically led working groups organised around major themes of care, recommended a series of initiatives to increase the profile of quality across the system and emphasised the crucial role clinical leadership will play in making this happen. For example, it deals with new incentives to reward higher quality care by providers, outlines a new era of transparency around quality and new quality reporting requirements (including the development of national measures which cover the whole field, not just infection). It also explored how to embed a culture of continuous quality improvement across the NHS. It sets out a vision where care moves closer to patients' homes, and where patients only go to hospital when hospital-based care is needed. Much more can be done in the community and while 'polyclinics' are controversial (not least among clinicians), it is inevitable that in the future, more care will be delivered out of hospital, which is both cheaper and more convenient for patients. Clinical leadership will be central to finding, and transitioning to, new models of care.

References and further reading

Black, C., Flory, D., Crump, B., Bundred, S., Calkin, C. and Carter, P. (2009) *Clinicians and Finance: Improving Patient Care*. http://www.audit-commission. gov.uk/SiteCollectionDocuments/AuditCommissionReports/NationalStudies/ 20090206CliniciansAndFinanceREP.pdf (accessed 2 March 2009).

Blakemore, K. and Griggs, E. (2007) *Social Policy: an Introduction*, 3rd edn. McGraw-Hill International, New York.

Committee of Enquiry into the Cost of the National Health Service (1956) *Report of the Committee of Enquiry into the Cost of the National Health Service* (Chairman: C. W. Guillebaud) Cmd 9663. HMSO, London.

Corrigan, P. (2005) Size matters – making GP services fit for purpose. *New Health Network* http://www.newhealthnetwork.co.uk/Content.asp?id=216 (accessed 6 April 2009).

Corrigan, P. (2009) *Health Matters*. http://www.pauldcorrigan.com/ (accessed 6 April 2009).

Darzi, A. (2008) *High Quality Care for All: NHS Next Stage Review Final Report*. Department of Health, London.

Department of Health (1989) *Working for Patients*. HMSO, London.

Department of Health (2002) *Securing Our Future Health: Taking a Long-Term View* (The Wanless report). Department of Health, London.

Department of Health (2002) *Reforming NHS Financial Flows: Payment by Results.* http://www.dh.gov.uk/en/Consultations/Closedconsultations/DH_4016901 (accessed 20 April 2009).

Department of Health (2009) *About Practice Based Commissioning.* http://www. dh.gov.uk/en/Managingyourorganisation/Commissioning/Practice-basedcommissioning/DH_4138698 (accessed 27 February 2009).

Department of Health and Social Security (1976) *Sharing Resources for Health in England: Report of the Resource Allocation Working Party.* HMSO, London.

Gaffney, D., Pollock, A. M., Price, D. and Shaoul, J. (1999) PFI in the NHS: is there an economic case? *British Medical Journal*, **319**, 116–19.

Griffiths, R., Betts, M., Blyth, J. and Bailey, B. (1983) Letter dated 6 October 1983 to the Secretary of State, Norman Fowler. *NHS Management Enquiry.*

HM Treasury. *Public Private Partnerships.* http://www.hm-treasury.gov.uk/ppp_pfi_stats.htm (accessed 4 April 2009).

Jones, K. (1972) *A History of the Mental Health Services.* Routledge, London.

Medical Services Review Committee (1962) Report of Medical Services Review Committee: Summary of conclusions and recommendations. *British Medical Journal*, **2**, 1178–86.

Monitor (2008a) http://www.monitor-nhsft.gov.uk/ (accessed 29 March 2009).

Monitor (2008b) *How the Assessment Process Works.* http://www.monitor-nhsft.gov.uk/home/becoming-nhs-foundation-trust/how-the-assessment-process-works (accessed 16 March 2009).

Mutuo, University of Birmingham (2008) *Membership Governance in NHS Foundation Trusts: a Review for the Department of Health.* http://www.dh.gov.uk/en/Publicationsandstatistics/Publications/PublicationsPolicyAndGuidance/DH_086374 (accessed 23 March 2009).

NHS Choices (2009a) *About the NHS.* http://www.nhs.uk/NHSEngland/aboutnhs/Pages/About.aspx (accessed 6 April 2009).

NHS Choices (2009b) *Hospital Choice.* http://www.nhs.uk/nhsengland/choices/pages/Aboutpatientchoice.aspx (accessed 5 March 2009).

NHS Confederation. *About Primary Care Trusts.* http://www.nhsconfed.org/Networks/PrimaryCareTrust/Pages/AboutPrimaryCareTrusts.aspx (accessed 27 February 2009).

NHS Connecting for Health (2009) *Choose and Book.* http://www.chooseandbook. nhs.uk/ (accessed 8 March 2009).

NHS London. *What We Do.* http://www.london.nhs.uk/what-we-do (accessed 1 March 2009).

Office for National Statistics (2008) *Expenditure on Healthcare in the UK.* http://www. statistics.gov.uk/articles/nojournal/ExpenditureonHealth08.pdf (accessed 15 April 2009).

Rivett, G. C. (2009). *National Health Service History.* http://www.nhshistory.net/ (accessed 4 April 2009).

Taylor, S. and Field, D. (2007) *Sociology of Health and Health Care*, 4th edn. Wiley-Blackwell, London.

White, T. (2006) *The Specialist Registrar and New Consultant Handbook*, 3rd edn. Radcliffe Publishing, Oxford.

Wikipedia (2009) NHS Strategic Health Authority. http://en.wikipedia.org/wiki/Strategic_Health_Authority (accessed 27 February 2009).

PART 2

What do you need to know to become an effective clinical leader?

You could argue that the rather complicated political and economic history of the NHS has no place as a core subject in the already crowded undergraduate and postgraduate medical curricula. But surely a basic working knowledge of the NHS is relevant – even essential – given that the NHS as a system is still likely to be a lifelong employer for most graduates from medical school. Not understanding the system's ways of working and constraints is just one of the divides between 'us and them' which this book aims to bridge.

The second part of this book moves on from understanding how the organisation operates to consider how you as an individual can operate more effectively as a clinical leader, whether or not you currently occupy a formal management role (or ever aspire to). This will involve a review of how leadership can be taught through the Medical Leadership Competency Framework (NHS Institute for Innovation and Improvement) as well as understanding the influences of personality and group dynamics on leadership styles.

Clinical leadership as a driving force to shape the future of the NHS will not come about if all we do is send trainees on week-long externally run courses or other similar 'sheep dip' approaches to leadership development. It will only flourish if clinicians themselves take ownership and accountability for how the service is run, creating a powerful social movement for change. Achieving this requires a commitment to the long-term development of the leadership skills and competencies required (through on-the-job placements and other in-house training), combined with a knowledge and awareness of how the NHS system operates.

This book is grounded in the growing body of international research that supports the assertion that clinical leadership improves the performance of healthcare organisations. There is a long road to travel to move from an evidence base, through undergraduate and postgraduate curricula, to professional recognition and status for career paths in clinical leadership. It is hoped that this book will go some way to overcoming the sceptical mindset that some clinicians may have about the value of spending time on leadership, relative to the immediate and often urgent value of direct patient care. It is hoped that the following chapters demonstrate that clinical leadership has positive implications for patient care, as well as professional success, rather than being superficially dismissed as 'going over to the dark side'.

CHAPTER 4

Teamworking and clinical leadership

Emma Stanton and Clare Chapman

The notion of teams and teamwork instinctively feels like a good thing in healthcare, particularly if you add a dash of multidisciplinarity and a splash of patient centredness into the mix. Teams feel familiar and safe because they are how our education system and early life experiences work. The *Next Stage Review* (2008) (see Chapter 3), placed delivering healthcare in teams across patient pathways at the core of improving quality of care. This chapter aims to educate the aspiring clinical leader about which aspects of teamworking in healthcare will make a difference to the quality of care a patient receives. It draws on evidence from management, psychology and health services research. It will cover how teamworking in healthcare influences patient safety, the effectiveness of healthcare and patient experience.

One of the most common sources of leadership failure is a failure to differentiate between whether *adaptive* or *technical* change is required. Technical problems require technical solutions (incremental changes on current ways of working). But many of the challenges currently facing the NHS demand new responses – a different set of behaviours – known as adaptive change. Historically, the NHS has prioritised investment in training individual technical skill rather than developing adaptive skills, such as teamwork and leadership (Flin *et al.*, 2009). To allow clinical leadership to flourish means giving up some security and confidence in what we know to enter a period of adaptive change.

Group dynamics

Although individuals influence groups, the groups themselves have an even more powerful influence over the individuals within them, and therefore knowledge of group dynamics is essential for a clinical leader, as the following evidence demonstrates.

The psychologist Kurt Lewin introduced the term 'group dynamics' in 1939, following classic studies on different styles of leadership. Schoolchildren were assigned to one of three groups with an authoritarian, a democratic or a *laissez-faire* leader. The children were then led in an arts and crafts project where the effects of different styles of leadership were assessed in terms of the functioning and social climate of the different groups (Lewin *et al.*, 1939).

Authoritarian leaders provided clear expectations for what needed to be done, when it should be done and how it should be done. Decisions were made independently with little input from the group. The children in autocratically led groups were dependent on the leader and more self-centred relative to their peers. Although authoritarian leadership can be useful in situations where there is little time for group decision-making, such as managing a cardiac arrest, this leadership style can be controlling, bossy and dictatorial. In healthcare, teams run in dictatorial fashion have been shown to be less likely to report medication errors than those more horizontally organised (West *et al.*, 2006).

Democratic (or shared) leadership is generally the most effective leadership style that clinical leaders should aspire to adopt. In democratic leadership, responsibility for decisions is spread throughout the team and team members are actively engaged. Leaders offer guidance to the group but also participate and encourage input from other group members. When led democratically, the same children showed more initiative, friendliness and responsibility. They also worked better and continued to work in the leader's absence, demonstrating a high level of engagement.

Laissez faire leaders offer little or no guidance to the group and leave decision-making up to the group members. Although this style can be effective if group members are highly qualified in an area of expertise, as may be the case in multidisciplinary healthcare teams, in Lewin's study this style was shown to be the least productive. The children made more demands on their leader, showed little cooperation and were unable to work independently.

From Lewin's research, democratic leadership is shown to be the most effective leadership style, but this conclusion is too simplistic, and warrants further consideration. There is agreement from different industries about the 'organisational context' in which quality improvement techniques are most likely to be effective. In healthcare, this requires the involvement of health professionals, especially doctors (Marshall, 2009). Clinical leaders in healthcare organisations, through bridging the divide between 'them and us', are able to more effectively align improvements in the quality of care with wider organisational strategy.

Defining teams and teamworking

A leader cannot be a leader without at least one follower. As has been discussed in the Introduction, one of the skills that transforms a manager into a leader is the ability to exert an above-average influence on other members of the group. There is no hard and fast rule about the optimal size of a healthcare team; it is possible for hundreds of people from different disciplines to be coordinated together in a team.

Teamwork in healthcare can be defined as

> a dynamic process involving two or more health professionals with complementary backgrounds and skills, sharing common health goals and exercising concerted physical and mental effort in assessing, planning or evaluating patient care. This is accomplished through interdependent collaboration, open communication and shared decision-making. This in turn generates value-added patient, organisational and staff outcomes. (Jelphs and Dickinson, 2008)

West and colleagues (1998) suggest three criteria for a group to be considered a team: the group needs to have a defined organisational function and identity; the group must possess shared objectives or goals; and the team members must have interdependent roles. Teams in healthcare will vary significantly, from primary care to mental health or respite care, in terms of their structure, purpose, task, setting and members. Frequently, healthcare teams are fluid and lack clear boundaries, which makes robust research and an understanding of the collaborative processes involved more complex.

The cross-fertilisation of ideas involved in working across boundaries promotes innovation. Innovation may be defined as the introduction of new and improved ways of doing things at work (West *et al.*, 2003). The group setting is believed to provoke a higher level of cognitive stimulation, which leads to additional ideas. A significant study of two independent samples of healthcare workers (66 breast cancer teams and 95 primary healthcare teams) showed that multidisciplinary teams were positively related to the quality of team innovation, providing the teams had good team processes. Interestingly, the size of the team was also positively related to innovation quality and quantity in both samples (Fay, 2006).

Table 4.1 summarises the antecedents, attributes and consequences of teamwork. Antecedents are events prior to the occurrence of a concept, while consequences occur as a result of it and have been divided into results for health professionals and for patients, as well for as the organisation. Attributes are the desired characteristics of teamworking in healthcare (Xyrichis, 2007).

Table 4.1

Antecedents	Attributes	Consequences

■ Two or more health professionals
■ Open communication and information sharing
■ Understanding of professional roles
■ Common health goals
	■ Concerted effort
	■ Interdependent collaboration
	■ Shared decision-making
		■ Health professionals
		  – Job satisfaction
		  – Recognition of individual contribution and motivation
		  – Improved mental health
		■ Patients
		  – Improved quality of care
		  – Value-added patient outcomes
		  – Satisfaction with services
		■ Healthcare organisation
		  – Satisfied and committed workforce
		  – Cost control
		  – Workforce retention and reduced turnover
		  – Higher organisation performance

The World Health Organization encourages teamworking in healthcare to promote the quality and efficiency of public health. There is growing evidence from health services research that there is more to improving quality than the technical aspects of care. Technical aspects of care refer to the appropriate application of professional knowledge and skill to provide healthcare, whereas interpersonal aspects of care involve both the relationship between patients and healthcare professionals as well as the contextual aspects of care (Flin *et al*., 2009). The importance of the organisational context has been demonstrated by a study into a sample of 52 hospitals in England which revealed that, after controlling for prior mortality and other confounding factors (such as the ratio of doctors to patients), the greater use of human resource management (people management) practices has a statistically significant relationship to reducing patient mortality. This suggests that hospital performance could be significantly improved by implementing human resource management techniques, such as training and appraisal systems and encouraging employees to work in teams (West *et al*., 2006).

For the majority of healthcare employees, team-based structures are the norm. However, it is not enough simply to work in a team. If team inputs (antecedents) and processes (attributes) are weak, then pseudo-team-based working

(PTBW) results; this appears to be *negatively* related to organisational performance. Pseudo-teams are generally large and have a weak or non-existent requirement for interdependent working. Team members do not meet regularly to review performance and the 'teams' do not have shared objectives. In the NHS, around 90% of staff report working in teams, but less than half (around 40%) of the total report working in entities that meet the criteria of a team (with shared objectives, interdependent working, regular meetings and small to moderate size) (Dawson, 2009).

A study of over 70,000 individuals in 173 acute hospitals in England showed that working in pseudo-teams is associated with reduced safety at work and reduced psychological well-being. These findings are important for aspiring clinical leaders to understand that there is no guarantee of team effectiveness simply by having a number of people working together within a clinical setting. For a team to be effective, it requires the right mix of people performing the task in a coordinated manner, with regular effective communication, in the context of clearly understood shared objectives, known as goal orientation. When a team lacks goal orientation and does not communicate effectively or work collectively, it becomes a pseudo-team (Dawson, 2009).

Communication

Although communication is something we do all the time, it is worth remembering that 70% of the message is non-verbal communication (Mehrabian, 1971), the words themselves are only 7% of the message (the tone of delivery constitutes the remaining 23% of the message). In the NHS, communication problems are often magnified by working in different locations; with diverse information systems that are unable to communicate with each other. The exponential growth of email as a form of communication between team members brings with it the risk of streams of unfocused and unnecessary emails that can be time-consuming and can obscure important priorities. The leader acts as a role model for how communication operates within the team (Barling, 2008).

This book has been created by a group of junior doctors who are learning to think and communicate in different ways through mentoring relationships with senior leaders in the NHS, many of whom are not clinicians. In this way, lines of communication traversing hierarchies and disciplines are being developed and traditional hierarchical barriers overcome.

Poor communication is a key barrier to effective teamworking. Acronyms are often a source of misunderstanding, so at the risk of introducing yet another acronym, the 'SBAR' model offers an approach to improve communication with a focus on patient safety. SBAR is a standard procedure within the aviation industry that is increasingly used as a systematic approach to improving the reliability of handovers in clinical medicine (Flin *et al.*, 2009).

- **Situation**: a concise statement of the problem. For example, 'I am calling about Child X who has increasing difficulty in breathing'.
- **Background**: relevant and brief information related to the situation. 'Child X is an ex-premature baby, who has not had her vaccination against Respiratory Syncitial Virus this year'.
- **Assessment**: analysis and consideration of options. 'She has a high respiratory rate, and signs of respiratory distress, although she is currently maintaining her oxygen saturation'.
- **Recommendation**: action. 'Child X needs to be admitted for monitoring and supportive treatment'.

Decision-making

In order to make the best decisions about healthcare, it is important for clinical leaders to have an understanding of the power of conformity in groups, as demonstrated by the 'Asch Paradigm' (1955).

In this experiment, a subject was placed in a group of stooges and asked to judge the length of a line. Figure 4.1 shows one of the pairs of cards used in the experiment. The card on the left has the reference line and the card on the right shows three comparison lines. Members of the group were invited to say which line was the same length as the reference line and to give their answers out loud, before the study participant. When all the stooges gave the wrong answer, the subject was more likely to agree with this view even though

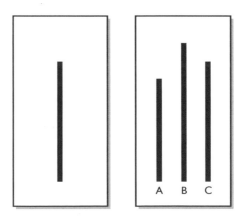

Figure 4.1 Experiment to illustrate the Asch Paradigm.

the correct answer was obvious. The pressures of conformity increase with group size, unanimity of the group decision and, crucially for the hierarchies of healthcare, perceived high status of the other group members. Vulnerability to conform is decreased by intelligence, self-esteem and self-reliance.

Many decisions in healthcare are made by groups rather than individuals, in board rooms, multidisciplinary meetings or on ward rounds. Group polarisation refers to the tendency of people to make decisions that are more extreme when they are in a group compared to the decisions the same people would make when deciding alone or independently. This means that when teams are making decisions about patient care, if an individual opinion is more prone to risk-taking it is possible the group decision will be riskier. Likewise, if the individual is more conservative, this will result in a more conservative group decision (Wright, 2003).

Team decision-making does not mean that every member of the team needs to be involved in all decisions. However, it is important for teams to have an agreed process for making decisions. For example, in psychiatry, responsibility for the care of referrals to a multidisciplinary team is distributed among the clinical members of the team. Contrary to the notion that doctors always dominate group discussions, Gair and Hartley (2001) found that doctors were more likely than other healthcare professionals to have their proposals questioned and were more likely to accept decisions contrary to their initial suggestions. The value of teams truly making decisions together is that it creates collective ownership which enhances commitment to implementing the outcome.

Groupthink is the desire to achieve consensus and avoid disagreement in group discussions (Janis, 1982). Groupthink classically occurs when a group of individuals meets in isolation from outside influences and lacks systematic procedures for identifying the advantages and disadvantages of a particular course of action. Highly cohesive groups are more likely to engage in groupthink, and so, in healthcare, ensuring multidisciplinary representation in teams and non-executive directors on boards tends towards creating 'cognitive diversity' and avoiding the hasty, irrational decisions associated with groupthink. The implications of this for clinical leaders are for them to be aware of the symptoms of groupthink that include an illusion of invulnerability and morality, pressure on dissenters to agree, self-censorship of dissent, collective rationalisation and the avoidance of considering alternative views. Being aware of these signs, encouraging open debate and playing 'devil's advocate' can help to guard against groupthink. During group discussions, it is worth bearing in mind that in mixed-sex groups, males have been consistently found to talk more, interrupt more and raise topics for discussion more than female members (Wright, 2003).

Including patients and their carers in the healthcare team means paying attention to their preferences and values, and to their knowledge of their condition and of the treatment they are receiving. A formal way of doing this is through shared decision-making which is the process of interacting with patients to come to values-based choices when the various options available have features that individual patients may value differently. Patient decision aids have been shown to improve both the quality of the decision as well as preventing overuse of options that informed patients do not value. At the time of writing, shared decision-making is underutilised in the NHS (O'Connor, 2004).

Safety

The 2003 NHS staff survey (Health Care Commission, 2004) showed that the greater the number of staff working in well-structured teams, the fewer the errors, near-misses and injuries that occurred.

As discussed, teams in healthcare are often multidisciplinary and consequently the members of the team are usually trained and educated separately. There is a risk that team members may not always appreciate each others' strengths and weaknesses because they have not been trained together. The Institute of Medicine (2006) suggests that team training programmes should be established, particularly in critical care areas such as Accident and Emergency and operating theatres. Proven methods for team training include crew resource management techniques from aviation, including simulation.

Crew resource management (CRM) originated from NASA who found that the majority of aviation accidents were due to human error, mainly around interpersonal communication, leadership and decision-making in the cockpit. The goals of CRM are enhanced situational awareness, increased ability to recognise a discrepancy between what is happening and what should be happening and improved communication through reduction in hierarchy-related barriers. CRM encourages informality between crew members by using forenames rather than professional titles and surnames.

CRM tells team leaders that having their judgement questioned need not be threatening (by contrast it may save them from making a catastrophic error), and can teach team members effective ways to question instructions. Although there are similarities between team issues in aviation and healthcare, effective training for healthcare teams should not be based on adopting these training technologies too literally, but rather on adapting them to ways of working in healthcare settings (Flin *et al.*, 2009).

Leaders should encourage their team members to develop psychological safety, which is a 'shared belief that the team is safe for interpersonal risk taking' (Edmonson, 1999). In order for this to happen, individuals need to feel confident that they will not suffer for speaking up. Mutual trust and respect amongst team members takes time to develop – a particular challenge for clinical leaders in the NHS, where team membership changes frequently.

Conflict

The diversity of skills and abilities that group members bring together in a multidisciplinary team can lead to exceptional synergy, but groups frequently fail to live up to expectations and are brought down by dysfunctional processes.

Conflict arises when people see the world differently and incompatibly. Some degree of conflict is inevitable (and it can be positive, for example, in preventing groupthink and allowing problems to be discussed and alternative solutions considered). Conflict becomes destructive when it is counterproductive to the long-term goal. This is discussed further in Chapter 11.

Although a degree of inter-team conflict can be beneficial, such as through competition between wards to achieve the lowest infection rates, this can be detrimental if it leads to a 'winners and losers' situation. Negative inter-group conflict can be reduced by rewarding teams, rotating membership of teams and ensuring high levels of communication between teams. Intra-team conflict commonly transitions through the stages of disagreement, confrontation, escalation, de-escalation and then resolution through negotiation and compromise.

Individual behaviour in teams

Chapter 5 covers aspects of personality and leadership. The best-known model for looking at individual behaviour in teams is Belbin's 'nine roles'. These were developed in response to the research question 'Why do some teams perform better than others?'. The characteristics assigned to each role are based on observation and have been well validated. Individuals complete a self-perception inventory to score points and are then allocated to a team role which has clearly defined strengths and weaknesses. You may well be able to recognise traits of people you have worked with in each of the nine roles (Belbin, 1981); see Table 4.1.

It is important to state that whilst an individual may have a tendency towards one role, the group dynamics and other characters present will define the actual role adopted in any particular circumstance.

Table 4.2 Belbin roles.

Role	Strengths	Weaknesses
Plant	Creative Imaginative Good at solving difficult problems	May ignore goals May become preoccupied
Resource investigator	Extrovert Enthusiastic Communicative	Overoptimistic May lose initial enthusiasm and interest
Coordinator	Mature Confident Good chairperson	Manipulative May delegate too much
Shaper	Challenging Dynamic Thrives on pressure	Can hurt other team members' feelings
Monitor-evaluator	Strategic Discerning	Lacks drive and ability to inspire others May be overly critical
Teamworker	Cooperative Diplomatic	Indecisive Easily influenced
Implementer	Disciplined Reliable Efficient	Inflexible Slow to respond to opportunities
Completer	Conscientious Timely	Overly anxious Poor at delegating
Specialist	Single-minded Self-starting	Focus too much on the detail rather than the bigger picture

Implications of teamworking for healthcare employees' wellbeing

Teamwork has been shown to be beneficial in terms of organisational performance, as well as creating more satisfied staff members who are more productive and less likely to be absent. Ineffective teamworking leads to lower staff satisfaction, negative behaviours and an inability to attract new and high-quality staff members which may impact negatively in terms of organisational performance and also team morale (Jelphs and Dickinson, 2008).

An NHS study carried out in 2000 showed that individuals working in clearly defined secondary care teams had lower levels of stress than those not working in teams or working in loose groupings. This is thought to be due to social supports and clarity of role reducing individuals' stress levels. The 2003 NHS staff survey found that although working in a team could lead to a higher level of staff injuries and stress, being in a well-structured team was associated with lower levels of staff injury and illness.

Failure of individuals to understand their role has been shown to be one of the biggest causes of stress in the work place; clinical leaders, therefore, should work to ensure that team members understand their own roles and behaviours (using concepts such as Belbin) as well as those of their colleagues.

Moods are easily transmitted between employees at the same hierarchical level in the workplace, a phenomenon known as 'mood contagion'. As a leader, it is important to be aware not only of how you interact with team members individually but also how team members interact between themselves. There is preliminary support for good leadership having a positive impact on the wellbeing of employees (Barling, 2008).

Barriers to teamworking

For teams to be maximally effective, they need the right people with the right skills. Clinical leaders will often inherit teams rather than being able to select their team according to their objectives. Different perspectives and skills can be productive, but can also be challenging. Teams that take time to meet and use their time wisely are more effective, but too often healthcare professionals do not feel empowered to prioritise time to invest in developing as a team.

In healthcare, individuals are likely to belong to more than one team with differing levels of engagement. A key problem for team formation is allegiance to a professional tribe. Creating good teams requires first overcoming the prejudices and behaviour inherent in this tribal mentality. Indeed, the more diverse and different team members are, the more likely it is that some individuals may have stereotypical or negative reactions towards one another. Diverse teams have the potential to deal with a range of issues, but in order to make the most of their teams' capabilities, clinical leaders need to ensure adequate investment in interrelations and communication methods.

'Tribalism' of health and social care professions leads to some professional groups trying to gain dominance over others in multidisciplinary settings. One of the suggestions for producing more effective teams is to encourage different professions to learn together at different stages of their careers. Different professions, such as doctors and managers, GPs and specialists, have their own languages, and have been socialised into specific ways of seeing and accepting the world. Healthcare teams in the NHS are frequently not highly evolved in terms of their functioning as teams because tribes, through professional hierarchies and functional boundaries, have acted as barriers to creating effective teams (West *et al.*, 2003).

NHS Constitution

The NHS differs from other industries in that over 60% of staff will still be with the NHS in ten years time. Following extensive qualitative and quantitative research, the NHS Constitution (Department of Health 2009) committed four pledges to all NHS staff:

- The NHS will strive to provide all staff with well-designed and rewarding jobs that make a difference to patients, their families and carers, and communities.
- The NHS will strive to provide all staff with personal development, access to appropriate training for their jobs, and line management support to success.
- The NHS will strive to provide support and opportunities for staff to keep themselves healthy and safe.
- The NHS will strive to engage staff in decisions that affect them and the services they provide, individually and through representatives. All staff will be empowered to put forward ways to deliver better and safer services for patients and their families.

In order to deliver the pledges of the NHS Constitution, there is a greater need for understanding and investing in enhancing teamwork within the NHS.

In summary, teams are important for healthcare and have been shown to improve the quality of care for patients. No one healthcare professional is likely to be able to provide all the support and assistance that, for example, a patient with chronic or complex needs requires. Teamwork is seen in healthcare as a way of working more effectively across tribal, internal and external boundaries to best meet the needs of the patient.

Simply creating a team-based organisational structure is not sufficient. Data has shown that although the majority of NHS employees believe they work in a team, less than half of them work in real teams, with the other half working in pseudo-teams, configurations which have been shown to be detrimental both to staff and to patient care. Clinical leaders face the challenge of ensuring they promote the formation of true teams which work effectively together to the benefit of patient care.

References and further reading

Asch, S. E. (1955) Opinions and social pressure. *Scientific American*, **193**, 31–5.

Barling, J. and Carson, J. (2008) Mental capital and wellbeing: making the most of ourselves in the 21st century. *Foresight Mental Capital and Wellbeing Project*. The Government Office for Science, London.

Belbin, M. (1981) *Management Teams*. Heinemann, London.

Darzi, A. (2008) *High Quality Care for All: NHS Next Stage Review Final Report*. Department of Health, London.

Dawson, J., West, M. and Yan, X. (2009) *Positive and Negative Effects of Team Working in Healthcare: 'Real' and 'Pseudo' Teams and Their Impact on Healthcare Safety*. Aston University (unpublished observations).

Department of Health (2009) *NHS Constitution*.

Edmonson, A. (1999) Psychological safety and learning behaviour in work teams. *Administrative Science Quarterly*, **44**, 350–83.

Fay, D., Borrill, C., Amir, Z., Haward, R. and West, M. (2006) Getting the most out of multidisciplinary teams: a multi-sample study of team innovation in health care. *Journal of Occupational and Organisational Psychology*, **79**, 553–67.

Flin, R., O'Connor, P. and Crichton, M. (2009) *Safety at the Sharp End. A Guide to Non-technical Skills*. Ashgate, Aldershot.

Gair, G. and Hartley, T. (2001) Medical dominance in multidisciplinary teamwork: a case study of discharge decision making in a geriatric assessment unit. *Journal of Nursing Management*, **9**, 3–11.

Haward, R., Amir, Z., Borrill, C., Dawson, J., Scully, J., West, M. and Sainsbury, R. (2003) Breast cancer teams: the impact of constitution, new cancer workload and methods of operation on their effectiveness. *British Journal of Cancer*, **89**, 15–22.

Institute of Medicine (2006) *To Err is Human. Building a Safer Health System*. National Academy Press.

Janis, I. L. (1982) *Groupthink: Psychological Studies of Policy Decisions and Fiascoes*, 2nd edn. Houghton Mifflin, Boston.

Jelphs, H. and Dickinson, H. (2008) *Working in Teams (Better Partnership Working)*. Policy Press.

Lewin, K., Llippit, R. and White, R. K. (1939) Patterns of aggressive behaviour in experimentally created social climates. *Journal of Social Psychology*, **10**, 271–301.

Marshall, M. (2009) *Applying quality improvement approaches to health care. British Medical Journal*, **339**.

Mehrabian A (1971) *Silent Messages*. Wadsworth, Belmont, CA.

O'Connor, A. (2004) Modifying unwarranted variations in healthcare: shared decision making using patient decision aids. *Health Affairs*, October.

Tyrer, P., Coid, J., Simmonds, S. *et al.* (1999) Community mental health teams for people with severe mental illnesses and disordered personality. *The Cochrane Library*, **4**.

West, M. A., Borrill, C. S., Dawson, J. F. *et al.* (2003) Leadership clarity and team innovation in health care. *The Leadership Quarterly*, **14**, 393–410.

West, M., Guthrie, J., Dawson, J., Borrill, C. and Carter, M. (2006) Reducing patient mortality in hospitals: the role of human resource management. *Journal of Organisational Behaviour*, **27**, 983–1002.

Wright, P., Stern, J. and Phelan, M. (2003) *Core Psychiatry*. Saunders, New York.

Xyrichis, A. and Ream, E. (2007) Teamwork: a concept analysis. *JAN Theoretical Paper*. Blackwell. Oxford.

CHAPTER 5

Personality and leadership

Colin Bicknell and Emma Soane

Several chapters in this book discuss the importance of leadership in the wider context of the NHS. In this chapter, we focus on the associations between personality and leadership, and consider the implications for developing effective clinical leaders in the NHS.

Developing leadership skills at all levels within an organisation is crucial to drive locally led improvement in quality. There is a requirement in the NHS both for leadership (setting the vision) and for management (organising people and tasks). This book sets out to prove that leadership is not reserved just for the people in the most senior positions. Within the NHS there is considerable scope for combining leadership and management at all levels, with doctors being particularly well placed to engage in leadership due to their skills, their role, and their wide-ranging networks that span professional and patient boundaries.

This chapter is organised as follows: firstly a discussion of how personality and leadership can work together to shape potential leaders and to develop leadership skills; then presentation of a case history of one very successful NHS leader to illustrate how an individual's self-analysis of their personality can improve their effectiveness as a leader. Finally, practical ideas for the reader to use to explore their own personality and their leadership style are discussed.

Leadership and personality

We start by exploring the nature of leadership: where it comes from, and how people get to be leaders in organisations. To understand the interplay between personality and leadership, there needs first to be an examination of why people wish to be leaders and how people enter leadership roles. Nigel Nicholson (2001) provides a useful perspective. He suggests that there are three drives for leadership. The first is the alluring status of leadership. People in senior positions have considerable benefits: including the ability to earn more, they are healthier, they live longer, and their work is meaningful. Second, people driven to leadership positions tend to have hard-wired dominance. There are genetically based individual differences in areas that are relevant to, and important for, leadership, such as drive, ability and constitution. These factors motivate people to become leaders and sustain them once they are in leadership positions. Energy and drive can even increase once people are in senior positions. Third, leadership positions fulfil archetypal roles. From our earliest days as infants we are raised in dependent relationships. This perspective stays with us through adulthood and perpetuates the need among us to be both leaders and followers.

Personality provides us with an approach to understand why some people are driven to attain leadership status, and why their ascent is supported by others. Personality is an important consideration since it tends to be relatively stable over adulthood, and is therefore a robust driver of characteristics relevant to leadership. Personality shapes individual work interests, preferences for dominance (and thus motivation for leadership positions), and leadership style. Personality is one important set of characteristics that helps us to address the questions of how people get to be leaders and, once in leadership positions, how they behave.

The most commonly used model of personality is the Five Factor Model. This is not meant to define personality but rather to aid understanding of personality and its effect on behaviour. The factors are as follows:

- *Emotional stability* is the degree to which people are calm, optimistic and resilient to stress versus feeling anxious and pessimistic.
- *Extraversion* is the degree to which people are sociable, assertive, enjoy a fast pace of life and are sensation-seeking versus being more reserved, leisurely, accommodating and quiet-seeking.
- *Openness* describes tendencies to think in concrete, down-to-earth ways compared with abstract, theoretical thinking and an interest in own and others' feelings.
- *Agreeableness* is the extent to which people are tough-minded, competitive and sceptical compared with being tender-minded, cooperative and trusting.
- *Conscientiousness* reflects goal-focus, self-discipline and achievement-striving versus a more relaxed, spontaneous approach.

Studies of leaders' personality have shown that there are three significant factors that characterise many leaders and contribute towards their leadership effectiveness. Leaders tend to be extravert and are characterised by openness and conscientiousness. This combination gives them social connections, the big picture perspective and the hard-working focus required to be effective and successful in leadership positions.

It is clear that personality is relevant to leadership. However, personality alone is not enough to explain how some people become leaders. In addition, the organisational context needs to be considered, and the complementary processes of selection and self-selection. People might have the drive to be a leader and set ambitions from their early career; both their personality and drive shape their motivation to become a leader. Nicholson summarises the three main processes through which people attain leadership positions:

- *Emergence*: people emerge through the organisation ranks. These people are characterised by their motivation and skills. An advantage of this process is that often there is consensus about the progress of this type of leader, as employees know whom they want as a leader. A disadvantage is that it is possible for dominant people to eclipse those with more talent.
- *Selection*: Elections or selection by others using a range of criteria can be used to select leaders. Managers from across an organisation and human resource (HR) specialists could contribute to this process. The advantage is that these can be fair and transparent. However, there need to be opportunities to recognise and acknowledge people who have flair and not just those who fit the mould.
- *Designation*: Leadership roles may be designated. The advantage of this approach is that leadership can be allocated fairly and sequentially to people of equal talent and expertise. An example is a university department where the head of department job is rotated among professors. A disadvantage is that leaders may not necessarily be driven to excel at their given role.

Within the NHS, each of the above three processes occurs. The relative prevalence of a particular approach depends on the traditions and specific demands of the department or organisation concerned. In each case, however, the process needs to be examined frequently to ensure that it is indeed promoting the person best suited for the job.

All processes of leadership selection or designation need to consider the acquisition of leadership skills to increase leaders' effectiveness. One of the prevailing approaches to understanding leadership, assessing leadership skills, and providing a platform for leadership development is the transactional and transformational leadership model. In this model the term *transformational* does not refer to organisational change, as described in Part 1 of this book. Here, *transformational* refers to the way that leaders move followers toward new values and a new vision. The term *transactional* refers to the sets of transactions that leaders and followers are engaged in.

The transactional and transformational model is intended to cover the full range of leadership behaviours that can be considered as arranged along a continuum. At one pole we have fully transformational leaders who generate exceptional performance as well as having high standards of morals and values. In contrast, at the opposite pole, we have the *laissez faire* leader. This is someone who is disengaged from their role, who does not take on responsibilities and will not give direction or support. Note that this is different from a delegating role, since *laissez faire* leaders have little involvement at any level and will not provide support. *Laissez faire* leaders have a profound impact on group dynamics, as discussed in Chapter 4.

Looking at the model in more detail, the initial building block is proactive transactional leadership. This is the set of exchanges between leaders and followers that are important to organisational functioning – for example, clarification of responsibilities and objectives, and giving rewards for fulfilling obligations. Rewards can range from a straightforward 'thank you' to formal employee recognition schemes, bonuses and benefits, such as time *in lieu*. This type of leadership is necessary in organisations, yet rarely results in exceptional performance. Something more than just the exchange of positive reward for work done is required to achieve outstanding performance, this is called transformational leadership. Transformational leaders have a set of additional skills and attributes. These include, first, raising the level of awareness of followers about the importance of achieving valued outcomes – a vision – and the required strategy. Second, leaders encourage followers to transcend their own self-interest for the sake of the team, organisation or larger collective. Third, leaders expand followers' need to improve themselves and their awareness of what they are attempting to accomplish.

Transformational leaders have four important sets of skills. This type of leader:

- Provides inspirational motivation. Leaders give followers a clear sense of purpose that is energising. This skill is often accompanied by leaders' charisma that draws followers to them.
- Is an idealised influence. They act as role models for excellent performance and ethical conduct which builds identification with the leader and their articulated vision.
- Creates intellectual stimulation. They enable followers to question the tried and tested ways of approaching problems, and encourage them to innovate.
- Shows individualised consideration. They focus on understanding the needs of followers individually and work continuously to help people to develop their full potential. In larger organisations, transformational leaders establish a culture of individualised consideration so that managers at all levels can operate on this basis.

The transformational and transactional model has been well researched and has been applied successfully to leadership development. Its current prominence rests on evidence that transformational leadership does indeed contribute to strong performance. Furthermore, the model provides a range of skills that can be learned. As with any skill set, development of transformational leadership skills is more likely to be effective when individuals are motivated to change their behaviour. Organisations and development coaches assist the learning process by helping leaders to plan their development, learn how to accomplish development, and to transfer their learning to their job. The role of coaching is discussed in more detail in Chapter 12.

The preceding review has shown how personality and leadership can be understood as conjoined processes involving characteristics, learned skills, and optimal organisational processes. There now follows a case study of a highly successful leader who embodies these characteristics. The purpose of this case study is to illustrate how transformational leadership can be achieved in practice. It provides examples that might be useful to clinicians interested in developing their leadership capacity, and doing so from both clinical and non-clinical role models, such as Cally Palmer.

Case study

Cally Palmer is the CEO of The Royal Marsden NHS Foundation Trust. She has been working in her current post for ten years and has spent a number of years progressing through hospital management roles in several hospitals prior to this.

Cally agreed to complete a personality assessment and to be interviewed about her personality and leadership style. Here the focus is on her personality, and how she has developed an effective leadership style that fits both with her personality and her organisation.

Cally's personality was assessed using the NEO PI-R (Costa and McCrae, 1992). This is a 240-item questionnaire and is one of the most comprehensive measures of personality available. The items are clustered into 30 facets of eight items each, yielding six facets in each of the big five factors of personality. To see how Cally's personality and leadership style fit together, the transactional and transformational leadership model was used as a basis for the interview questions. The data has then been organised to illustrate the main areas of leadership, and following this there is a reflection upon how Cally's personality contributes to her style of leadership.

Inspirational motivation

Cally has a positive perception of her leadership style based on her feedback from colleagues and leadership development programmes.

> I think I'm open, visible, accessible and decisive. I'm quite a strong leader so I have to be careful that I don't dominate. This is something that I'm very aware of. I inspire quite a high degree of loyalty. I think that people like working with me. I'm also very passionate about the Hospital and the NHS, and people identify with that, particularly in an organisation like this. I'm not neutral or grey.
>
> I have a very strong vision for the hospital which came from listening to staff, observing, and then setting a strategy which has been in place for the past five years. The themes, I think, are the correct themes and they have been consistent.

Idealised influence

Cally emphasised the importance of being a role model to the employees in her organisation.

> I think it is important that people consider that the Chief Executive is a person of integrity, fairness and openness. I am at pains to display this to all groups of staff. I go and talk to nursing staff, and other staff – we talk about our attitudes to the hospital and its future. We talk about the importance of creating a strong patient environment and I think that people think that focus is the right focus. A doctor once said to me, 'I don't always like your decisions, but I know that you are fair. If the decision is no, I know why it's no'.

Intellectual stimulation

Cally recognised the intellectual challenge of her role and of her employees. She is clear about what her contribution to problem-solving can be, and knows how to create an environment in which innovation can occur.

> The first thing is having a dialogue about their ideas and encouraging staff to contribute to the creative piece. Creating ideas and options that inspire people is important. However, we make sure that we don't have

so many complicated ideas that we can't deliver them. There is always something going on. We deliver service changes or improvements fast, which allows people to feel they are contributing to an exciting future.

People here are clever, specialised, and they are very highly motivated so it's not that hard a job to engage them. But it's keeping in touch with them, making sure that you do deliver. I think the other thing that motivates people is sharing the problems with them as well as the exciting things. It's giving them [staff] the passion and drive to do it, and thanking them regularly and assiduously when they have pulled it off.

Individualised consideration

In a large organisation such as this London hospital, it is not possible for the CEO to know all of the staff. However, Cally gets to know as many people as possible and, importantly, encourages leaders at all levels to do the same.

> People really like it when I tell them personally what a great job they have done. The Chief Nurse and the Medical Director are also very good at this so we are a tight, good team that takes the time and trouble to make sure that there is a personal touch when thanking people.

In addition to building a large network around the hospital, Cally provides a highly individualised career development programme.

> We are assiduous in terms of development and support. In terms of development we expect to support staff practically and financially with study leave and professional development. If they have a plan it's not just a token; we do it properly so people feel they are supported in their development. The other thing – it is quite a family environment, so people feel that they are treated as individuals in terms of their careers in the NHS. There is a lot of personal knowledge and stability in this environment which allows that to happen.

Managing problems

It is clear that Cally is a transformational leader. She is continually proactive and could not be characterised as *laissez faire*. When discussing dealing with problems, she presents a very effective process that fits with her leadership style.

I tell people when there are problems. I don't sweat in my office and think how am I going to do this? I'm very open. I get a group of people together, whomever I think needs to influence the problem, and we'll sit and talk about it. I pay a lot of attention to translating it into a language that means something to them. So, rather than saying we've got a money problem this year, I say it's really important that we have a surplus of X million because we want to build that extra facility, don't we? It's an obvious thing to say, but translating the message into language that is important to people in their daily lives provides them with an incentive. I tend to put an optimistic spin on things so things are do-able for people. I think that's quite important.

The quotations above demonstrate that Cally is a truly transformational leader. When considering Cally's personality and her development it can be seen how she has attained such an achievement. Looking at each of the five personality factors from p. 68 in turn, it is clear that Cally's character is optimised in her role, a position that Cally has created intentionally through self-awareness and targeted learning.

(i)   Beginning with considering *emotional stability*: Cally's profile showed that she is highly resilient and competent in coping with stress.

    I'm quite a strong person, that's what people say.

(ii)   Cally is very *extravert*. This drives her need to work with other people and her skill in understanding what other people need from her as a leader. Her extraversion also encompasses a strong preference for taking the lead rather than being in the back seat. She is willing and happy to take responsibility and be in charge.

(iii) In the *openness* dimension, Cally was found to be moderately interested in abstract thinking. She enjoys a mix of practical reality and big ideas. She is very interested in her own and others' feelings. She is aware of these preferences and has used her awareness to shape her career direction. Her comments reflect our earlier point that getting the fit between people and organisations right contributes to their effectiveness.

    I am very interested in strategic direction, but as it relates to my hospital here. What I engage with less is general policy development at the Department of Health. So I'm aware of that. I've been trying to do more policy work and push myself in that direction but it's not my natural territory.

(iv)   Cally has several moderate scores in the *agreeableness* factor. Such a profile is often associated with tendencies to negotiate, and this was reflected during our interview. An area in which Cally has a particularly strong characteristic is competitiveness. Cally is aware of her competitive nature and works hard to see that her competitiveness is applied positively to benefit the hospital.

(v) Finally, turning to *conscientiousness*: Cally has several moderate scores in this factor. She acknowledges the importance of work–life balance. However, Cally is extremely driven. She strives hard for success and is very self-disciplined.

> I am very focused and quite driven. I think on my feet fast and can move fast intellectually, but sometimes I haven't done a lot of nuts-and-bolts preparation. I know other chief executives who have a style where they read more and prepare more and think about their points. I'm much more instinctive than that. I don't know if it's a personality thing or a time-availability thing, but my life is very finely balanced between home and work and so I do operate very quickly, which means I prepare very, very carefully for some things, but on other things I'm quite instinctive. I think I have good judgment. I am very experienced in the world that I work in so I can work faster than I could have done 10 years ago or even 5 years ago probably. Also that is probably one of the reasons why I stay in organisations. It's easier to work faster somewhere where you have trust and you have built relationships, and that's important to me. I don't like flying in doing something for two years then flying off again. That's never been my thing.

Cally has also taken a focused approach to her personal and professional development from her early career to her current position.

> I've always loved my work. There hasn't been a single period where I have wanted to leave. For whatever reason it has ticked all my boxes in terms of personal wish and need.
>
> I suppose life teaches you that you start off working 80 or 90 hours a week but that is not sustainable, so I've had to learn how to manage my time for maximum effect. I've had the insight to realise that I'm not a Department of Health policy person. I love working in a hospital. It gives me a huge buzz. I like the immediate delivery. I'm very practical. I love the people stuff. I would hate to sit in an office somewhere where I didn't have that range of contact with people who interest me. So I can sit with doctors or scientists and I won't understand what they are talking about if it's some abstract scientific theory, but I can understand enough to say, 'OK this is how you do it, make it a reality'. That is where I am valuable. I really enjoy that.

Overall, Cally's profile shows an excellent fit between her personality and the demands of her job. Her resilience to stress, competitiveness and drive to succeed combine well with her sociability, genuine interest in other people and ability to mix strategic ideas with practical delivery of high quality services. She has learned to work to her strengths by combining self-awareness with structured training.

Leadership development

Previous sections have noted the relevance of both characteristics and skills to effective leadership. While individual personality characteristics are relatively stable, existing skills can be enhanced, and new skills learned. Next the focus is on what needs to change when people become leaders, and how development programmes can be structured.

At the individual level, it is useful to set leadership learning within the context of cognitive development. One of the most significant processes that underpins leadership growth is the changes in patterns of thinking that characterise the move from novice to expert. Clinicians work through this process during their training to become experts in their field, readily able to solve a wide range of problems. A similar process needs to occur for specialist clinicians to become effective clinical leaders. This process has been characterised as a move from System 1 thinking, i.e. conscious and rule-based information processing, to System 2 thinking which is more automatic and subconscious. This change occurs with increasing experience. In practice, this means that skilful leaders are able to assess information, draw on their extensive experience, and reach appropriate decisions rapidly.

The transition from clinician to leader is best achieved through a structured development programme, as discussed in Chapter 12. Leadership development research has identified several factors that increase the success of such programmes. Recent articles by academics and practitioners have emphasised the importance of structured programmes that combine well-designed curricula, useful theories and opportunities to put learning into practice. Learning is optimised further by organisational cultures that support forums for discussion of new ideas, openness to collaboration across professional boundaries, and application of innovative practices. Chapter 8 discusses a range of structured programmes available to clinicians in training to develop their leadership skills by stepping outside standard clinical training.

Leading yourself

So far this chapter has considered the nature of leadership, taking individual differences in personality into account. The following list contains practical suggestions as to how the reader can apply the content of this chapter to enhancing their self-awareness and advancing their development as a leader.

1. Consider what motivates you. Why do you want to be a leader?
2. Ask for feedback from peers, superiors and team colleagues. Keep in mind that no one is great at everything. Listen to other people's opinions. Create positive opportunities for feedback and show that you are acting on advice.
3. Find out what you enjoy and what you can excel at.
4. Find people who inspire you. Look for positive role models among senior leaders. You might find that your own senior leaders are excellent role models, such as Cally. It may be useful to look beyond the people you work with. Reading biographies, the business press and interviews with successful leaders can provide a wealth of information about leadership.
5. Consider a coach or a mentor. This type of support might be offered to you as part of a leadership development programme. If not, ask a trusted colleague or friend if they will act as a mentor to teach you specific skills, or as a coach to aid your professional development. This is discussed further in Chapter 12.
6. Set development plans with clearly defined goals, actions required to meet goals, and timescales. Ensure that your goals are measurable and achievable and provide an attainable challenge.
7. Examine your environment, considering which organisational characteristics motivate you, and which demotivate you. Consider the possibilities for making changes to the way that you organise your work so as to optimise your effectiveness and motivation.
8. Continue your professional development. Revisit these questions, keep learning, and continue to ask for feedback.

The development of an effective clinical leadership structure, spanning leadership of teams and departments at local, regional and national levels, requires a complex programme reflecting individual needs and encouraging raised self-awareness. There is much work to be done within the NHS developing effective leadership training programmes both within institutions and at a national level.

One of the patrons of the newly established NHS National Leadership Council is Daniel Goleman, author of *Emotional Intelligence*. In Goleman's view, emotional intelligence is:

the ability to perceive emotions, to access and generate emotions so as to assist thought, to understand emotions and emotional knowledge, and to reflectively regulate emotions so as to promote emotional and intellectual growth.

Emotional intelligence includes self-awareness and it is hoped that this chapter has assisted you to reflect on your own strengths and weaknesses in terms of personality and leadership, in order to enhance your effectiveness.

References and further reading

Bass, B. and Avolio, B. (1990) The implications of transactional and transformational leadership for individual, team, and organizational development. *Research in Organizational Change and Development*, **4**, 231–72.

Bass, B. (1985) *Leadership and Performance Beyond Expectations*. Free Press, New York.

Costa, P. T. and McCrae, R. R. (1992) *NEO PI-R and NEO-FFI Professional Manual*. Psychological Assessment Resources Inc, Odessa, FL.

Darzi, A. (2008) *High Quality Care for All: NHS Next Stage Review Final Report*. Department of Health, London.

Digman, J. M. (1990) Personality structure – emergence of the 5-factor model. *Annual Review of Psychology*, **41**, 417–40.

Judge, T. A., Bono, J. E., Ilies, R. and Gerhardt, M. W. (2002) Personality and leadership: A qualitative and quantitative review. *Journal of Applied Psychology*, **87**(4), 765–80.

Goleman, D. (1996) *Emotional Intelligence: Why it Can Matter More Than IQ*. Bloomsbury, London.

Nicholson, N. (2001) *Managing the Human Animal*. Random House, London.

Northouse, P. (2007) *Leadership: Theory and Practice*, 4th edn. Sage Publications Inc.

CHAPTER 6

Ethics and clinical leadership

Robert Elias

Some might ask why a book on leadership contains a chapter on ethics. The answer is straightforward. Leadership is often, perhaps always, about trying to do, and bring others to do, the right thing well. This chapter explores in more detail how ethics and leadership overlap. It is meant to stimulate the reader to self-reflection and to encourage discussion and debate.

The NHS Leadership Qualities Framework says surprisingly little that is explicit about values, yet personal integrity is one of the five key personal qualities identified. This is described as a 'sense of commitment to openness, honesty, inclusiveness and high standards' (NHS Institute for Innovation and Improvement 2006). Few would quarrel with the need for integrity defined in this way. But values, described as ethics, morals or simply 'doing the right thing', are surely far more essential to the role of leadership than the framework explicitly states.

The relationship between leadership and ethics is ambiguous. This is because value judgements permeate both what leaders do and how we think about leaders. 'Good' leaders are those who are considered to make the 'right' decisions. We respect good leaders, we value their honesty and integrity and we are persuaded to follow them. It is challenging, and arguably not possible, to separate out the ethical component of what it is to do good work, be it clinical practice or any other kind of work, from the activity of doing that work. Attempts to separate the ethical component of leadership from the day-to-day learning and doing of leadership are similarly doomed to fail. This is partly because leadership encompasses such a wide array of activities that there is no single ethical formula to identify all the ethical issues that may arise for a clinical leader.

The complexity of the activity of leading is one reason why ethical analysis of leaders and leadership is difficult. Another reason for this difficulty is suggested by philosophical approaches to ethics – the way values can be identified and can influence decisions and behaviour – which question the possibility of stating general rules or principles in ethics that are practically useful.

The aim of this chapter is to ask what 'doing ethics' offers leaders. 'Doing ethics' is defined very loosely for the purpose of this chapter. It is reflection on and analysis of values and the way they are embedded in and influence behaviour. A leader will obviously be concerned with the way values relate both to their own behaviour and to the behaviour of the people they are seeking to lead. An important difference between doing good work and being a leader is that leaders aspire to lead others to do good work. Sometimes the work of a leader will be defined successfully influencing others to do good work. Sometimes it will be sufficient to lead by example, and do good work for others to see. Usually, leaders need to have an explicit understanding of influences on the behaviour of themselves and others. They may articulate it only to themselves, or in addition to others. An ability to articulate what it is that makes a behaviour or an outcome good is critical to successful leadership, as discussed in the preceding chapter on personality and leadership.

There is not the scope in this chapter for a detailed treatment either of individual values or of the many philosophical approaches to ethics. In any event, ideas and examples of what constitutes good leadership abound throughout this book. This chapter aims to introduce the reader to possible approaches to thinking about values. These different approaches form a resource for thinking about values in the complex world of clinical leadership. Below are two case studies based on challenges that all clinical leaders face, selected to illustrate how these approaches are helpful.

Two ethical challenges for the aspiring clinical leader

1. *Self-interest and self-sacrifice*

   A prerequisite for becoming a leader is that you are successful. Those who successfully shimmy up the greasy pole have, by definition, demonstrated a degree of self-interest. Success within a profession usually demands a degree of conformity in the form of behaviour which is acceptable to those established higher in the hierarchy. It is also the job of a leader to bring about change where change is needed, to identify inadequacies and to put the delivery of high-quality patient care above the interests of themselves or their colleagues. The very notion of becoming a clinical leader can generate conflict between the needs of the individual to conform (in order to progress) and the interests of the patients they aspire to serve.

2. *The patient in front of you and the population*

   The tension between the needs of any individual patient and the limited resources of any individual healthcare organisation are not unfamiliar to any practising doctor. All healthcare professionals, at whatever stage in their careers, aspire to do the best for the patient who is sitting in front of them. The desire to provide the best possible treatment for this individual in the here and now – the same treatment as anyone would want for their mother – will often conflict with the limited resources available. This tension is particularly acute for a clinical leader. Leading change to make the allocation of resources within an organisation fairer could result in the patient sitting in front of you losing out. How will you reconcile sending a woman with kidney failure back home to a country where there is negligible dialysis provision (which is potentially your duty as a leader within your organisation) with your duty as a doctor, or indeed your duty as a person?

Resources

Rules and principles: formal training and guidance

Formal training in ethics for junior doctors comes from two main sources. Ethics is taught at medical school, and guidance on ethical matters is offered by professional bodies, most notably the General Medical Council. There are other specific opportunities for training in medical ethics. Numerous courses are available. Clinical ethics committees offer advice and occasionally education. However, there is no requirement that clinicians will use these opportunities.

Ethics teaching

Medical ethics retains a strong dependence on the 'four principles' approach of Beauchamp and Childress (2001). These are: respect for autonomy, beneficence, non-maleficence and justice. The benefits of this approach include the introduction at an early stage of a clear, memorable framework to act as an aid to analysis of the ethical issues involved in a clinical situation. The main drawback of a principle-based approach is that in order to be universally applicable, such principles have to be very general and thus they provide limited insight for the complexity of real life. There is also a danger that teaching medical ethics as a separate component in a curriculum leads to a sense that ethics can somehow be separated from the day-to-day business of clinical practice. These two criticisms of the teaching of medical ethics parallel the difficulties in teaching leadership skills.

Leadership and clinical practice both embody such diverse activities that seeking to identify specific ethical principles that will apply across the whole spectrum of those activities risks generating principles which have no real power to explain or influence behaviour. Some leadership theorists would suggest that leadership cannot be taught without reference to the person who is leading and the situation they find themselves in. This view of leadership is sometimes called situationalism. Its parallel in ethics is called moral particularism, which holds that moral judgements are not dependent on the existence of moral principles. A strongly case-based approach to medical ethics can be consistent with moral particularism.

Ethics teaching in medical schools is increasingly sophisticated, and reflects concerns about principle-based approaches and the segregation of ethics from clinical practice. Theories other than the four principles above are discussed and used. In this way, ethics teaching is woven vertically and horizontally through the curriculum and opportunities are taken to examine and encourage reflection on the ethical aspects of day-to-day clinical practice. In reality, any formal training in ethics will account for only a very small proportion of a clinician's response to a given difficult situation.

Take the first ethical challenge described above. The ethical prerogative to put patients first, above your own self-interest, is clear. But how can you go about restructuring the running of an outpatient clinic, for example, in the face of intransigence from senior colleagues? It might be argued that this is no longer an ethical question as it is clear what should be done. How to achieve the objective is not a question of ethics. However, the activity of attempting to bring about ethical ends is in itself an activity that requires ethical judgement. For example, deciding between charging into the chief executive's office to complain about the mistreatment of patients in clinic A and, alternatively, proposing an audit of current patient waiting times and satisfaction is itself an ethical activity. One way is certainly better than another, largely because it is more likely to be effective. Appreciating that one set of behaviours will be more effective requires an understanding of the motivations of the people involved, in terms of the values they bring to their work. There is more at work here than can be readily summed up for generic clinical training.

Guidance from professional bodies

The General Medical Council has responsibility for the 'self-regulation' of doctors in the UK. It publishes guidelines on the standards of behaviour expected from doctors (General Medical Council, 2006). It also provides guidance on specific ethical issues and on broader aspects of practice, such as consent (General Medical Council, 2008).

For a clinician seeking to take a lead in the running of a department, the GMC guidelines on the duties of a doctor may seem distant from the daily dilemmas about resource allocation, fair treatment of colleagues, and hospital politics. The guidance may be clear and fair, but not specific enough to be helpful. Rights and duties are often used when there is a failure of some sort. For many, the GMC provides a bottom line well below their expected level of function, without the sensitivity to engage with complex daily ethical issues.

Despite the criticism of rules-based approaches in medical ethics, their progenitors in moral philosophy – deontological and consequentialist approaches – have dominated ethics because of their intuitive appeal and their success. Rules can be necessary. In the second challenging situation (to crudely oversimplify from recent well-publicised cases), there would seem to be no reason to send a woman with kidney failure to a country without dialysis other than because the NHS cannot provide for everyone. Many would say that this is reason enough. In the interests of everyone, some people must lose out. The aim is for the greater good of the greater number; difficult decisions and personal tragedies are, sadly, inevitable.

Virtue ethics through role models

Inspiring individuals can have a huge impact on our behaviour and on our ideas of what it is to be a good clinician or a good leader. Relationships with role models can be formal or informal, close or distant, specific or general. You may learn a particular way of describing a procedure to patients by seeing someone communicate with a patient exceptionally well. You may read about someone at the height of their career in a newspaper and be inspired to follow in their steps. You may be allocated a mentor on a leadership programme, such as 'Prepare to Lead', or an educational supervisor to oversee your training.

It goes without saying that not all role models are good role models. It is for an aspiring leader to decide what kind of person and leader they want to be. Given the complexity of clinical practice and the importance of role models in developing our sense of what is good practice, the questions 'What kind of person do I want to be?' and 'What would a good person do in these circumstances?' are important ones. Some would argue that thinking about what it is that makes people and their actions virtuous is a more profitable approach to ethical problems than one based on rules or principles. Such an approach within ethics is called virtue ethics and has experienced a recent resurgence in the field of professional ethics.

Virtue ethics has long been present in both Western and Eastern philosophical traditions. Aristotle's ethics is taken by most contemporary Anglo-American philosophers as the starting point for theories of virtue ethics. The appeal of virtue ethics is illustrated by contrasting its practical usefulness in real situations with the limitations of rules and principles. The first ethical challenge about balancing self-interest and self-sacrifice can be more usefully answered by thinking what a virtuous person would do rather than by appeal to principles.

However, these approaches are not mutually exclusive. Some of the philosophical approaches to ethics directly oppose one another, such as moral particularism and consequentialism. But in practical terms, these are ways of thinking about what is the right thing to do. It is possible for your thinking to be informed by all of these approaches. In the same way that development in clinical practice is not dependent on one way of learning, so your development in ethics can be informed through a variety of approaches.

Sociology and anthropology

While formal training and guidance offer frameworks for thinking about ethics and minimum acceptable standards of behaviour, the strongest influence on behaviour lies in the environment in which we are trained and work. Our responses are shaped by the 'moral landscape' of our work (Eckenwiler and Cohn, 2007). That moral landscape is shaped in turn by many factors, such as peers, profession, organisational cultures and our interactions with members of other professions and disciplines.

It is only recently that bioethics has become an explicit topic for study by sociologists. Armstrong (2006) considers the histories of public health and medical ethics. The history of medical ethics is looked at not in its own terms but 'in its close relationship to the form and nature of the medical profession'. A great deal has been written about the sociology and anthropology of medicine that pertains to the moral landscape of clinical work. It has seldom been clearly identified as 'doing ethics' although two eminent sociologists of medicine, Bosk (2008) and Fox (with Swazey, 2008), have published books reflecting on the relationship between their work and bioethics. There is a growing trend in favour of 'empirical ethics' (de Vries, 2006). Empirical ethics relates the conclusions of philosophical medical ethics to day-to-day clinical practice, either through studies of practitioners' and patients' attitudes or through sociological and anthropological work.

To illustrate the importance of sociology in understanding behaviour and therefore its role in the leader's ethical armoury it is useful to refer to a seminal paper written in 1979 by Jeffrey entitled 'Normal rubbish: deviant patients in casualty departments' (Jeffrey, 1979). This paper describes how healthcare professionals typify patients. It is a demonstration of how behaviour that professionals see as 'normal' can be behaviour that is laden with value judgements.

Anyone who has worked in a busy hospital will be familiar with clinicians' tendencies to refer to 'the stroke in bed twenty' or 'the really interesting case in bed sixteen'. Many social scientists have claimed that they are not seeking to pass judgement on these kinds of behaviours, but to describe and explain them. In fact, much sociology of medicine has been both implicitly and explicitly critical of the dehumanising effects of doctors' behaviour in referring to and interacting with patients.

Whether or not the intent is explicitly normative, the endeavour of describing the behaviour of healthcare professionals and uncovering hidden influences on behaviour is essential for the activity of 'doing ethics'. Critical scrutiny of clinical practice is necessary to identify those behaviours, and those influences on behaviour, which are positive and those which are not acceptable. There is a strong tendency within professions to presume that the way things are done – what is – is the way that they should be done – what should be. Philosophers are often keen to point out that 'you cannot get an ought from an is'. In order to uncouple what ought to be from what is and to enable change for the better, which is the leader's aim, it is necessary to see afresh 'what is'. This is where sociological approaches to medicine can be of benefit.

In the first challenging scenario above, an understanding of the role of professions in constraining behaviour could be extremely helpful. For example, awareness that colleagues are concerned to lose professional status through the restructuring of services in favour of patients may enable you to see not only what the right thing to do is but also ways of going about it. A good leader will seek to realign the professional aims of colleagues so that they converge with the best interests of patients.

Humanities

It is not just professional roles and responses that can be seen in day-to-day clinical work. Natural, human responses to decisions and interactions are everpresent. Patients seek trusting relationships with their carers. The question 'What would you do doctor?' is a common one. Professionals sometimes shy away from talking about death and dying for profoundly personal reasons, or indeed form a rapport with patients by virtue of their personal investment in their care. The same is true of leaders. An appreciation of the human and the humane way to act is essential.

The humanities offer insights into the human condition that biomedical science lacks. Literature, art and music have the potential to reveal aspects of human suffering that science cannot. A humane leader needs, as Denis Healey famously described it, a 'hinterland'.

Along with the insights afforded by reading literature, an appreciation of narrative can be more specifically helpful in healthcare (Greenhalgh, 1999). The narrative form is the medium of a great deal of medical work. The patient's 'history' forms the basis of almost any meeting between healthcare professional and patient. Discussions between professionals about patients often centre around a 'case history'.

If the relationship between the ethics of clinical practice and the humanities is unclear, it is perhaps largely because of the current predominance of a principles-based approach, with particular emphasis on the importance of autonomy. As with the sociology of medicine, art contributes to a broader and deeper understanding of human behaviour, which is essential for the exercise of good judgement.

In summary, adopting a philosophical approach to ethics in healthcare may be unfamiliar to many readers. This chapter aims to help clinical leaders think about ethical values in their clinical practice and leadership roles.

For the clinical leader, the challenge to do the right thing is always present. To meet that challenge, the ability to articulate the overt and hidden values at work and to use your experience and knowledge to resolve them – to 'do ethics' – is essential.

References and further reading

Armstrong, D. (2006) Embodiment and ethics: constructing medicine's two bodies. *Sociology of Health and Illness*, **28**(6), 866–81.

BBC News (2008) *Anger after removed Ghanaian dies*. http://news.bbc.co.uk/1/hi/wales/7306345.stm (accessed 6 August 2009).

Beauchamp, T. L. and Childress, J. F. (2001) *Principles of Biomedical Ethics*, 5th edn. Oxford University Press, Oxford.

Bosk, C. L. (2008) *What Would You Do? Juggling Bioethics & Ethnography*. University of Chicago Press, Chicago.

De Vries (2006) Social science and bioethics: the way forward. *Sociology of Health and Illness*, **28**(6), 665–77.

Eckenwiler, L. A. and Cohn, F. G. (2007) *The Ethics of Bioethics: Mapping the Moral Landscape*. Johns Hopkins University Press, Baltimore.

Fox, R. C. and Swazey, J. P. (2008) *Observing Bioethics*. Oxford University Press, New York.

General Medical Council (2006) *Good Medical Practice*. http://www.gmc-uk.org/guidance/good_medical_practice/index.asp (accessed 6 August 2009).

General Medical Council (2008) *Consent: Patients and Doctors Making Decisions Together*. http://www.gmc-uk.org/guidance/ethical_guidance/consent_guidance/index.asp (accessed 6 August 2009).

Greenhalgh, T. (1999) Narrative based medicine: narrative based medicine in an evidence based world. *British Medical Journal*, **318**, 323–5.

Jeffrey, R. (1979) Normal rubbish: deviant patients in casualty departments. *Sociology of Health and Illness*, **1**(1), 91–8, 106–7.

NHS Institute for Innovation and Improvement (2006) *NHS Leadership Qualities Framework.* http://www.nhsleadershipqualities.nhs.uk/ (accessed 6 August 2009).

Stanford Encyclopedia of Philosophy (2009) http://plato.stanford.edu/ (accessed 6 August 2009).

CHAPTER 7

Education and training for clinical leadership

Bob Klaber and David Bridle

In order for clinical leadership to flourish in the NHS there needs to be education and training of the highest quality for future leaders. The new competency-based clinical frameworks are designed to enable individuals with strong clinical skills to progress more rapidly through training, whilst the clinical academic programmes that have been introduced will enable the identification and support of future academics. Historically there has been an absence of programmes to identify, nurture and support trainees showing early leadership potential. In addition to Chapter 8, this chapter will introduce recent initiatives endeavouring to meet the need to develop future clinical leaders.

> Contrary to the opinion of many people, leaders are not born. Leaders are made, and they are made by effort and hard work
> *Vince Lombardi, 1913–1970, professional football coach*

This well-known quote touches on the topic at the core of this chapter. Becoming a leader is not solely due to an inherent capacity. It requires effort and practice to develop, as does training for a clinical specialty. Leadership development needs to become integrated and embedded in the education and training of clinicians, including doctors, from an undergraduate level.

There is a general feeling amongst consultants that whilst the many years of their clinical training gave them both depth and breadth of clinical experience and expertise, preparation for many of the leadership, management and educational roles was much less comprehensive, and in many cases almost non-existent. For many doctors and clinicians, these issues only start coming into focus during the final months of their training as they look to prepare themselves for consultant interviews and posts. There are a significant number of interview preparation and management training courses available, and some of these include information on leadership development. Whilst these undoubtedly offer some excellent opportunities for learning, steps are being taken to integrate and embed leadership development throughout the whole training period rather than leaving it until the end. If other aspects of clinical training were left to a two-day course, abstracted from day-to-day working, in the last few weeks before becoming a consultant there would be an outcry. This chapter explores why and how leadership education and training are being integrated alongside clinical training.

Lessons can be learnt from other sectors and industries about embedding leadership learning into the workplace. The Toyota Way is often cited, which is based on the key pillars of seeking out continuous improvement alongside respect for people. The origins of Toyota leadership go back to the Toyota family who developed several key principles. 'Toyota Way Principle 9' states 'grow leaders who thoroughly understand the work, live the philosophy and teach it to others'. This is not aimed as a programme for a small group of high-fliers but as a culture of learning and development for everyone at Toyota, which underpins the whole ethos of this hugely successful company. Diageo is another company which has invested in building the leadership capabilities of their workforce to drive business performance. Their year-long leadership programme is built around key standards which ask their developing leaders to be authentic, to create possibilities, to bring the company purpose to life, to create the conditions for people to succeed, to consistently deliver great performance and to grow their own capability and experience. This is supported by a process of executive coaching, and those who have previously been through the programme are instrumental to the facilitation of it in subsequent years. This commitment to leadership development does not come cheaply, but in both of these examples the business performance validates the investment.

As a long-term approach, investing in leadership learning could undoubtedly bring similar rewards within the health sector, and there are some examples of this from across the world. In their paper 'Engaging doctors in Leadership: what can we learn from international experience and research evidence', Ham and Dickinson highlight Denmark as a country where doctors are explicitly involved in leadership roles. This is supported by a detailed ongoing programme of competency-based mandatory leadership training at postgraduate level which includes a 10-day leadership course provided by the Danish regions and the National Board of Health. Consultants are additionally offered a five-day leadership course after appointment. The authors also highlighted evidence from the Netherlands of a robust, systematic approach to leadership development. Leadership training was not included in the undergraduate curriculum in any of the countries reviewed.

Another important question addressed in different ways throughout this book is whether leadership training should be given to all, or focused on certain individuals who show early signs of aptitude and desire to be leaders of the future. Answering this question involves a review of what leadership entails.

Clearly you cannot have several captains on board a ship arguing over which direction to sail.

In order to form a strong, functional team each member needs to be self-aware, to work well with others and to be able to critically evaluate their own performance. These are key leadership skills that all should be looking to develop at every stage of their career. This approach to 'shared leadership' is the focus of the work the Academy of Medical Royal Colleges and the NHS Institute for Innovation and Improvement have jointly undertaken in developing their excellent Medical Leadership Competency Framework (MLCF). Lord Darzi's Next Stage Review *High Quality Care for All* stated:

> Greater freedom, enhanced accountability and empowering staff are necessary but not sufficient in the pursuit of high quality care. Making change actually happen takes leadership. It is central to our expectations of the healthcare professional of tomorrow.

The MLCF picks up this challenge by describing a broad range of leadership competencies that doctors need to achieve by becoming involved in the planning, delivery and improvement of services for their patients. This is explained in more detail below.

> The Medical Leadership Competency Framework (MLCF) is built on the concept of shared leadership where leadership is not restricted to people who hold designated leadership roles, and where there is a shared sense of responsibility for the success of the organisation and its services. Acts of leadership can come from anyone in the organisation, as appropriate at different times, and are focused on the achievement of the group rather than the individual. (Introduction to Medical Leadership Competency Framework)

The MLCF was first published in 2008 and drew on a wide range of evidence and resources. These included reviews of the literature on medical leadership and engagement, analysis of specialty medical curricula and comparative analysis of national and international leadership competency frameworks already in existence. There was also consultation via use of reference groups, focus groups, semi-structured interviews and involvement from the Patient Lay Advisory Groups of the Medical Royal Colleges. Refinements in a second edition have been made (2009) after feedback from stakeholders and it is planned that further revisions will be made in the future to ensure it remains aligned with the latest thinking around health service needs and improvements.

The MLCF applies to all medical students and doctors and has been designed to have sufficient breadth to support leadership learning from the onset of undergraduate training through to the first few years of practice after training. It consists of five domains, within which a total of 20 key elements are described. These are detailed in Table 7.1.

The core ethos of the MLCF is to support doctors in their work of delivering services to patients, service users and carers. Which domains apply to an individual doctor will depend upon their career stage and the type of role they fulfil. For example, it is envisaged that the domains on 'demonstrating personal qualities' and 'working with others' will be initially developed during undergraduate training, whereas learning around the final domain 'setting direction' is more likely to occur in the latter years of postgraduate training and beyond. The authors highlight the MLCF as a key tool which can be used to help the design of training curricula and development programmes, highlight individual strengths and development areas through self-assessment and structured feedback from colleagues, and assist with personal development planning and career planning.

The Academy of Medical Royal Colleges and the NHS Institute for Innovation and Improvement have been involved in discussions with both the Gen-

Table 7.1 (Reproduced with permission from Academy of Medical Royal Colleges and NHS Institute for Innovation and Improvement 2009 *Medical Leadership Competency Framework*, 2nd edn. NHS Institute for Innovation and Improvement, Coventry)

Developing personal qualities	Developing self-awareness Managing yourself Continuing personal development Acting with integrity
Working with others	Developing networks Building and maintaining relationships Encouraging contribution Working within teams
Managing services	Planning Managing resources Managing people Managing performance
Improving services	Ensuring patient safety Critically evaluating Encouraging improvement and innovation Facilitating transformation
Setting direction	Identifying the contexts for change Applying knowledge and evidence Making decisions Evaluating impact

eral Medical Council (GMC) and the Postgraduate Medical Education and Training Board (PMETB) to explore ways in the MLCF could be integrated into the learning for both undergraduate students and postgraduate trainees as well as the continuing practice of more senior doctors. Work has begun with each of the Royal Colleges exploring how best to embed the MLCF into their curricula. However, the key to this exercise is not what it looks like on paper or within an e-portfolio; it rests on successfully mastering the practicalities of integrating the learning and assessment of these competencies into day-to-day experiences in the workplace.

There are a great number of practical examples of opportunities for learning and development within the MLCF, and as the tool is adopted by the different Royal Colleges these will undoubtedly be translated into a wider range of specialty specific examples.

Whilst there is value in trainees undertaking well-planned high-quality audit, the approach that 'every trainee must undertake an audit in every six-month posting' requires evolution. The vast majority of audits undertaken are poorly planned, inadequately supervised, fail to complete a cycle and lead to minimal learning, let alone serving to improve the quality of patient care. Indeed many would argue that they are tick-box exercises that should be re-shaped as quality improvement projects. Students and trainees should undoubtedly have the opportunity to get involved with audit activity during their training, but equally they should be given the opportunity to learn about patient safety issues, clinical risk, managing people and performance, implementing change and facilitating transformation. Table 7.2 details some practical examples of how this experience might be obtained. These ideas were generated by a group of postgraduate paediatric trainees during a workshop-based training exercise, facilitated by one of the authors of this chapter.

Whilst there is now a significant evidence base underpinning the reliability, validity and feasibility of many clinical examinations such as Objective Structured Clinical Examinations (OSCE), or the PACES examination used by the Royal College of Physicians, the development of assessments of leadership competencies is in its infancy.

Multi-source feedback is also sometimes called 360-degree appraisal. Coupled with high-quality debrief and facilitated reflection on the process, this offers the potential for real developmental learning; it is what underpins the leadership development strategies of companies such as Diageo. The biggest challenge is around feasibility. Most 360-degree tools require over ten raters, and even though many are supported by electronic technology, the total 'people hours' required for each individual's appraisal makes large-scale implementation of this style of assessment difficult. More feasible is the adaptation of the 'case-based discussion' style of workplace-based assessment that is beginning to be used to assess clinical skills at both undergraduate and postgraduate levels.

Table 7.2 Workplace opportunities to develop leadership skills as a post-graduate trainee.

- **Identifying areas for change**
  - Audit – leading to the implementation and evaluation of change
  - Consulting with clinical and management colleagues
  - Gaining senior management support and approval
  - Quality improvement projects

- **Rota management**
  - Encouraging contribution from others
  - Implementing and reviewing change
  - Interacting with consultants and fellow trainees
  - Learning about workforce management issues
  - Supporting teamworking
  - Open decision-making and empowering choice

- **Department induction**
  - Writing a guide to working in the department
  - Developing a guide to training opportunities
  - Focusing on key areas of patient safety (such as handover)

- **Guideline development**
  - Bringing in outside experience (for example, from previous posts)
  - Use of evidence-based practice
  - Reviewing the practice of colleagues; improving and instigating change

- **Teaching/education/supervision**
  - Tutoring/supervising – medical students/SHOs/other health professionals
  - Developing opportunities for multi-professional learning
  - Developing critique, feedback and debrief skills
  - Establishing and running simulation bases, resuscitation calls
  - Sharing ideas and learning with colleagues
  - 'Lesson of the week' – on handover sheet
  - Opportunistic teaching. For example, workplace-based assessments at night
  - Exam question writing/standard setting/examining

- **People and performance management**
  - Praise and recognition of excellence – saying 'thank you and well done'
  - Supervising/supporting/mentoring colleagues
  - Learning to say 'I don't know' – and role-modelling this

Table 7.2 (*continued*)

- ■ **Attending and contributing to meetings**
  - – Directorate meetings
  - – Risk management meetings
  - – Implementing junior doctors' meetings
  - – Representing trainees in training meetings
  - – Being involved in decision-making processes
  - – Improving team relationships and working practices
- ■ **Operational matters**
  - – Chairing of multidisciplinary team meetings
  - – Recognition of the clinicians role as a manager
  - – Role-modelling behaviour through clinical practice
  - – Comparing how things are done differently from Trust to Trust
- ■ **Service quality and improvements**
  - – Reviewing patient journeys
  - – Patient satisfaction questionnaires
  - – Talking to patients and learning from their experiences in hospital
  - – Reviewing morbidity/mortality data and measures to improve outcome
- ■ **Identifying key players in the Trust** – talking to them about their role
- ■ **Understanding Trust strategy** – attending Board meetings
- ■ **National Strategy** – helping with the 'on the ground' message (for example, around patient safety)

Leadership training for undergraduates

Prior to entering undergraduate medical training, the potential of leadership capability is considered as entry criteria. In its *Guiding Principles for the Admission of Medical Students*, the Council of Heads of Medical Schools recommends (Medical Schools Council, 2006) that the selection process for students by medical schools should attempt to identify core academic and non-academic qualities of a doctor; it states, amongst other criteria, that 'curiosity, creativity, initiative, flexibility and leadership are all desirable characteristics for the aspiring doctor'.

The various UK medical schools hold primary responsibility for the teaching and training which is provided to medical students. Although each medical school has substantial discretion on what to teach and how, the General Medical Council (GMC) provides the framework within which all medical schools must operate. This framework is detailed in the document *Tomorrow's Doctors*, which was updated in September 2009 and states:

> It is not enough for a clinician to act as a practitioner in their own discipline. They must act as partners to their colleagues, accepting shared accountability for the service provided to patients. They are also expected to offer leadership, and to work with others to change systems when it is necessary for the benefit of patients.

Tomorrow's Doctors details the areas that the GMC considers important and this influences what medical schools teach and how. The framework sets outcomes that graduates need to meet, and the updated 2009 version specifically details an 'overarching outcome' within which there is recognition of the importance of clinical leadership. The purpose of this outcome is:

> to make the care of patients their first concern in accordance with Good Medical Practice, applying their knowledge in a practical and ethical manner and *using their ability to provide leadership* and to analyze complex and uncertain situations. (Italics not in original)

This suggests an incorporation of leadership abilities at the heart of what a medical student should be developing through undergraduate training and fits with its integration throughout the curriculum as opposed to it being a stand-alone 'add-on'.

Within the body of this document, expected outcomes relating to the 'doctor as a professional' are detailed. Some attributes of leadership are specified here, notably to 'learn and work effectively in a multi-disciplinary team' by demonstrating the ability to take on different team roles, including leadership, and to 'deal effectively with uncertainty and change'.

Medical students are already offered clear guidance about the professional values expected of them. In the GMC publication *Medical Students: Professional Values and Fitness to Practise* there is advice that in order for students to demonstrate that they are fit to practise, they should develop and demonstrate teamwork and leadership skills.

Whilst the framework detailed in *Tomorrow's Doctors* highlights the importance of leadership development it does not detail how any of the outcomes should be achieved or assessed, leaving this up to individual medical schools to determine. The framework also recognises the undergraduate period of a doctor's education as only part of a continuum of education and training. This offers an opportunity for varied approaches to incorporate relevant leadership training experiences for medical students.

With reference to the Medical Leadership Competency Framework (MLCF) described earlier in the chapter, the two most obvious leadership domains to be focused on during undergraduate training are 'Personal qualities' and 'Working with others'. Whilst the other three domains (see p. 92) predominantly lend themselves to being developed further along in training, there are also some suggestions on how to start developing skills in those areas during the undergraduate years.

The examples below highlight the value of recognising and integrating this skill development in opportunities that arise routinely through training:

- Doing a presentation at the end of an attachment, making sure that you get feedback (Personal quality – developing self-awareness)
- Completing course requirements such as attendance and submitting work (Personal quality – managing yourself)
- Organising extra learning sessions (Personal quality – continuing personal development)
- Getting elected by other medical students to a position of responsibility (Personal quality – acting with integrity)
- Attending and participating in multidisciplinary team meetings (Working with others – developing networks)
- Building respect through holding office, for example, in student union (Working with others – building and maintaining relationships)
- Actively seeking a patient's perspective by completing a patient journey assignment (Working with others – encouraging contribution)
- Participating in various roles in group learning – including team leader, scribe etc. (Working with others – working within teams)

Leadership training for postgraduates

The United Kingdom is now placing significant emphasis on leadership development within the frameworks that govern and inform postgraduate training, in keeping with building on the undergraduate learning and development that has been detailed above. This is illustrated, for example, in the Foundation Programme, which is intended to provide a protected environment during the first two years following graduation from medical school, with a view to building up the new doctors' capacity to practise independently. A core competency under 'Working with Colleagues' in the Foundation Programme is described as:

- Foundation Year 1 – 'takes leadership role in the context of own competence when necessary'
- Foundation Year 2 – 'can show leadership skills where appropriate, but at the same time works effectively with others towards a common goal'

The remit for developing a single, unifying framework for postgraduate medical training (overseeing its content and standards) is part of the responsibility of the Postgraduate Medical Education and Training Board (PMETB) which has been operating in the UK since 2005. PMETB has been explicit about recognising significant current and anticipated changes in the environment in which medicine is practised. This includes changes that encompass society, patient expectations, advances in medicine, the changing workforce and service developments. PMETB has been undertaking a major review to consider how to incorporate these kinds of issues into planning for the future healthcare system. The review has four work streams, one of which is called *Educating Tomorrow's Doctors*, which has a remit to address medical education. This group has produced a report entitled *Educating Tomorrow's Doctors – Future Models of Medical Training; Medical Workforce Shape and Trainee Expectations* which highlights the need for future doctors to have more than just technical knowledge and skills. In particular it emphasises the importance of what have previously been called 'soft' skills, including leading a team and understanding healthcare management. As such it envisages that future doctors will be 'not only technically adept but are confident in providing holistic patient-centred care as leaders and key members of multi-disciplinary teams'.

It follows that the report's three recommendations in the leadership area are that appropriate work-based multi-professional team learning should be encouraged, that all doctors need to have an understanding and knowledge of leadership and management on a day-to-day basis in the health service (for example through leading a multidisciplinary team and managing resources), and that the trainees with the requisite interest and aptitude should have opportunities to develop themselves for leadership and management roles.

As in the case for undergraduate training, it is important to integrate the experience and training for leadership and management into the wider course of postgraduate training as far as possible. Suggestions on how to do this are made in the Medical Leadership Competency Framework, which offers many varied ways to develop in the five domains. Specific tasks or roles can be sought out to provide introductions to key skills. The MLCF demonstrates that there is considerable scope for taking the initiative to broaden experiential learning through engaging in local opportunities that arise. Table 7.2 illustrates how readily accessible such opportunities are for postgraduate trainees. For individuals with a particular interest in developing their leadership skills there is much to be gained from exploring opportunities to shadow, or have formal attachments or internships with, their Trust's medical director.

The focus throughout this chapter so far has been on identifying and using opportunities to develop leadership skills in a practical manner, embedded within ongoing clinical training. This emphasis is deliberately adopted because this approach offers significant opportunity for gradual and robust development of the leadership skills needed.

As stated at the beginning of the chapter, bespoke courses and other opportunities for doctors in training to develop leadership skills can enhance their experience and capabilities, supplementing the work-based learning opportunities available. Well known examples in the UK include the King's Fund course on 'Management for Specialist Registrars', the 'Managing Life in the NHS' courses established by the London Deanery to educate clinicians about clinical governance, NHS South Central's 'Lead or be Led' programmes, and the highly interactive 'Politics, Power and Persuasion' courses run by Baroness Cumberlege. These types of course remain popular and extremely positively evaluated by participants, although they do have their critics. Whilst these courses are likely to cover the theory and science of leadership and the relevant context of the health service, there are some excellent courses that go further by also helping participants to explore their own attitudes, to understand themselves and how they relate to others better (for example, using the Myers–Briggs Type Indicator psychometric assessment) as well as giving opportunities for experiential learning.

Involvement with the Royal Colleges and Postgraduate Specialty Schools can enhance what has been developed and learnt in other arenas. There are other organisations, such as BAMMbino, which likewise encourage and nurture leadership development. Representative roles can be good experience, either on training committees or through the British Medical Association structures which include the Local Negotiating Committees. All of these organisations will provide different opportunities and support for postgraduate trainees to both experience and develop their leadership potential.

Mentorship and coaching are provided by some deaneries and SHAs and the value of these is discussed in Chapter 12.

This chapter has demonstrated that there are many and varied opportunities for postgraduate trainees to develop their leadership capacity in the context of their clinical training. It is vital that developing as a clinical leader and being a clinical leader become core to the day-jobs of some doctors. However, there are also paths to becoming a clinical leader which involve stepping outside standard clinical training, often temporarily. The next chapter examines these.

References and further reading

Darzi, A. (2008) *High Quality Care for All: NHS Next Stage Review Final Report.* Department of Health, London.

Foundation Programme (2007) *The Foundation Programme Curriculum.* http://www. foundationprogramme.nhs.uk/pages/home/key-documents (accessed 22 March 2009).

General Medical Council (2009a) *Medical Students: Professional Values and Fitness to Practise. Guidance from the GMC and the MSC.* http://www.gmc-uk.org/education/documents/GMC_Medical%20students.pdf (accessed 21 April 2009).

General Medical Council (2009b) *Tomorrow's Doctors*, rev edn. http://www.gmc-uk.org/tomorrowsdoctors (accessed 4 March 2009).

General Medical Council (2009c) *Tomorrow's Doctors. Outcomes and Standards for Undergraduate Medical Education.* http://www.gmc-uk.org/education/documents/GMC_TD_2009.pdf (accessed 1 September 2009).

Ham, C. and Dickinson, H. (2007) *Engaging Doctors in Leadership: What Can We Learn From International Experience and Research Evidence.* NHS Institute for Innovation and Improvement.

Liker, J. (2004) *The Toyota Way: 14 Management Principles from the World's Greatest Manufacturer.* McGraw-Hill, New York.

Medical Schools Council (2006) *Guiding Principles for the Admission of Medical Students.* http://www.chms.ac.uk/documents/RevisedAdmprinciplesNov2006MSCwording27.1.09.pdf (accessed 16 March 2009).

NHS Institute for Innovation and Improvement, Academy of Medical Royal Colleges (2008) *Medical Leadership Competency Framework*, 2nd edn. http://www.institute.nhs.uk/images/documents/MLCF%20May%202009.pdf (accessed 15 April 2009).

Postgraduate Medical Education and Training Board (2008) *Educating Tomorrow's Doctors – Future Models of Medical Training; Medical Workforce Shape and Trainee Expectations.* http://www.pmetb.org.uk/fileadmin/user/Content_and_Outcomes/Working_group_reports/Educating_Tomorrows_Doctors_working_group_report_20080620_v1.pdf (accessed 6 March 2009).

Spence, D. (2009) Comic Leadership. *British Medical Journal*, **338**, 887.

CHAPTER 8

Stepping outside standard clinical training

Claire Lemer

All too often medicine, for all its joys, can seem rather like an escalator. You step on at roughly the age of sixteen when you choose your GCSEs and seamlessly flow through medical school and postgraduate training to reach your final goal as a consultant, GP or associate specialist. The pressure of exams and continuous assessment, not to mention the need to publish, makes the journey seem akin to a tunnel. There is little time to contemplate what the final job will actually be like on a day-to-day basis and whether the skills that you are gaining as you progress are the ones that you will need.

As the previous chapter has discussed, postgraduate training is changing to become more applied and more focused. For example, in paediatrics, 2009 saw the first pilot of an 'exit assessment' designed to test not knowledge, but practical skills and management abilities.

The reality is that many new consultants feel unprepared to cope with the management and leadership tasks that they are faced with. Many feel frustrated that they are spending time away from their clinical work, which they have dedicated many hours of gruelling training precisely to do.

In the past, any desire to step outside the classical path of training would have been viewed by colleagues, deaneries and even colleges as slightly eccentric at best, and more likely actively discouraged. This despite many of the same individuals when they were juniors having voiced bewilderment and anxiety about what becoming a senior doctor brings.

For some it is this desire to ensure that they are trained for all aspects of their future roles that causes them to stop and think about management or policy or public health aspects of medicine. For others, it is a less defined awakening, spurred perhaps by an article, a patient experience or a non-work-related event, that encourages them to be more circumspect about planning their careers. In the USA and other countries there is much less of an assumption that medical graduates will remain smoothly on a 'classic' career track.

Whatever the cause, increasing numbers of junior doctors, facilitated by deaneries and colleges, are expanding their career choices and stepping off the escalator, at least temporarily, to pursue this knowledge and skills concurrently with medicine. Those who do this find that their life skills, confidence, knowledge and often their commitment to medicine are expanded and strengthened, frequently in unexpected ways.

The current situation that has arisen partly by design and partly by serendipity has created such an overwhelming array of options that it is hard to determine what is right for any given person. As so many of these options are new, it is difficult to find people knowledgeable enough about the opportunities to provide detailed advice. Perhaps the best advice that can be given to those in this position is to talk to as many people as possible about their fledgling aspirations. Talk to consultants who seem sympathetic, be really brave and approach a manager; talk to the college representatives or deanery leads, email people you have read about in the *BMJ* or BMA news. In short, part of making the leap between different worlds is about finding the courage to talk to people. It absolutely does not matter if you cannot crystallise exactly what you are looking for or why you are interested in management or policy. What matters most is that you take and make opportunities to find out how best to develop yourself.

In many ways the same techniques that GCSE and A-Level students apply to finding out if medicine is of interest to them, through work-shadowing, visits and career chats, are just as useful here. The experience of many junior doctors who have successfully stepped out of medicine, is that when they have been brave enough to approach senior leaders – even distinguished ones – the response has been welcoming and encouraging.

If you decide that time out of medicine, or gaining new experiences alongside medical training, is a good idea for you, the most difficult part is deciding what and how. One of the first decisions to be made is: do you want to take time out or do you want to 'dip a toe' into a different world continuing alongside standard medical training? Similarly, if the answer is to leap beyond medicine, when is it a good time to make this jump? Should it be at a natural break point such as between foundation training and ST or after completion of College exams? There is no right answer to this and the best advice is to act according to personal circumstances in discussion with deaneries and other relevant training bodies. It is important to discuss how the time out of training will be acknowledged. It may be possible in some situations for this to be an Out of Programme (OOP) arrangement. Similarly, whilst some believe that it is best to leave these types of experience for the latter stages of medical training, the counter-argument that earlier experiences can be more career changing or enhancing is not without merit.

The key to finding the programme or opportunity that best suits your needs is to start early. Many of the more formal programmes have long lead times – sometimes as much as 18 months in advance of the actual start date. Many require project outlines to be submitted at the initial stage, so in reality the lead time may be even longer. Less formal arrangements often take considerably longer than anticipated to iron out the creases.

The options outlined below are not meant to be comprehensive; rather they are illustrative of the types of opportunity that exist for people looking to add something to a traditional medical career path. Of course there are many opportunities for doctors in careers outside medicine: pharmaceuticals, medical devices, consulting and finance are just some of the best-trodden paths there are, but these are beyond the scope of this chapter. (It is important to note that for many these careers all too often lead back to healthcare in some form at some point.) Some options outlined below are open for doctors only, others for a variety of professions. Some are UK-based, others are international. Some fit in alongside medicine; others require time be set aside completely. The terminology pertaining to these experiences is confusing and overlapping. A fellowship may not be more academic than a secondment, and an advisory role may be more junior than the name implies.

The potential options include the following:

1. *Chief Medical Officer's Clinical Advisory Scheme*
   Developed from a pilot in 2008, the scheme now affords around 30 junior doctors in training the opportunity to spend a minimum of a year out of clinical practice. The scheme is based around the old-fashioned principle of medicine: apprenticeship. Doctors are seconded from their training to a range of organisations to work directly under the lead doctor within the organisation. To date, host organisations have included the Department of Health, National Patient Safety Agency, Strategic Health Authorities, Royal College of Physicians, the National Institute for Health and Clinical Excellence, Bupa and the Health Protection Agency. Mentors include the Chief Medical Officer, Medical Director of the NHS, and Regional Directors of Public Health. The scheme consists of day-to-day experiences within the organisation, learning sets to encourage personal development and sessions focusing on specific techniques or skills such as public speaking.

2. *Darzi Fellowships*
   Following on from the Next Stage Review, a number of SHAs have created opportunities for Junior Doctors to understand more about quality improvement and management. London has a pilot scheme under way this year that has over forty junior doctors spending a year working for the Medical Director of an NHS Trust (both PCT and Hospital) learning about the work of the medical director whilst being actively involved in a change management programme of their own. The programme has a strong academic component to support learning, with participants completing a Postgraduate Certificate 'Doctors as Managers' from Leeds University Business School.

3. *Other examples of SHA-based schemes*
    Along similar lines to the Darzi Fellowships, some SHAs have created opportunities for completing medical training alongside NHS management training. The first such cohort is currently under way in the North West SHA, where junior doctors learn about management alongside NHS management trainees and can also apply for multidisciplinary leadership fellow posts. Severn Deanery, and Kent, Surrey and Sussex Deanery have also initiated similar leadership schemes. Wessex Deanery has developed an alternative structure whereby interested individuals spend time outside the UK developing healthcare infrastructures. In London, the authors of this book originate from the Prepare to Lead scheme, which matches senior healthcare leaders to act as mentors to junior doctors who are interested in healthcare management. In addition to one-to-one mentoring the scheme has monthly sessions focusing on key aspects of management and leadership.

4. *Deanery school based schemes*
    As deaneries develop their existing structures into specialty-based schools, opportunities are being created for junior doctors to take part. Some, like paediatrics in London, have created 'shadow' functions to allow juniors to be actively involved. Schemes such as this enable individuals to learn new skills in a supported manner which may act as a springboard to other programmes.

5. *Harkness Fellowships in Health Policy*
    Begun in the 1920s, and run by the Commonwealth Fund in the USA, these fellowships were originally open to all graduates of UK universities. Set up by an anglophile, the expectations and regulations connected to the scheme were limited. Fellows were provided with a stipend and visa, and most importantly the time to explore a new country and grow as individuals. The alumni of the scheme have forged successful careers in varied paths: journalism, medicine, academia, creative writing, law and science. In more recent times, the fellowship has been realigned to focus on health policy and research. Around five applicants are chosen on an annual basis from the UK and join an international programme, with representatives from Switzerland, Germany, Holland, Canada, Australia, New Zealand and Norway. Each fellow and their family is supported to spend a year in the USA, dividing their time between research, under the guidance of a mentor of the fellow's choosing, and learning about health policy as a group.

6. *Health Foundation Fellowships*
    The Health Foundation is a UK-based not-for-profit organisation dedicated to improving the quality of UK healthcare. The charity offers a number of different fellowships.
    Leaders for Change is about supporting individuals from any professional background in healthcare who already have experience of, or

who are interested in, change management in a hospital environment. Participants do the scheme concurrently with keeping going in full-time work.

Quality Improvement Fellows are similarly connected to change management. Rather than being based in the UK, these fellows spend a year in the USA, based in Boston at the Institute for Healthcare Improvement (IHI), learning quality improvement methodology. As with the Harkness Fellowship, to which there are strong links, families are supported through a stipend, and a fundamental part of the experience is about developing networks and links beyond the UK.

7. *Fulbright Scholarship*
Some may prefer to gain new insights through academic study. There are many opportunities to achieve funding for such degrees within and beyond the UK. Perhaps the best-known fellowship to the USA for postgraduate education is the Fulbright Scholarship. Individuals compete to be chosen to spend up to a year in the USA, studying any subject at the university of their choosing. Successful candidates must also win a place at the academic institution at which they wish to study.

8. *MBA*
The formal study of business skills, through an MBA (Masters in Business Administration) is another option discussed in more detail in the following chapter.

Many of the above schemes were designed or built around the work of junior doctors who, often out of frustration, created opportunities for other like-minded colleagues. These schemes have often benefited from the insights of the very people they are aimed at, being at the heart of designing the programme. Equally, they have demonstrated that it is eminently possible and indeed feasible to create new paths and careers beyond the traditional hierarchies of clinical medicine. Organisations such as BAMMbino (the junior doctors division of the British Association of Medical Managers – BAMM) have created a national network of junior doctors interested in future careers in healthcare management and leadership that can also act as a portal for sharing ideas about stepping outside standard clinical training.

In many ways, now is the golden age for clinical leadership. There is both central support and encouragement through the National Leadership Council and also local engagement by junior doctors moving with the direction of travel. The emphasis may be moving away from thinking about stepping outside medicine completely towards deciding what non-traditional leadership and policy experiences to add to clinical careers and when to make the leap.

References and further reading

Darzi, A. (2008) *High Quality Care for All: NHS Next Stage Review Final Report.* Department of Health, London.

Foundation Programme (2007) *The Foundation Programme Curriculum.* http://www. foundationprogramme.nhs.uk/pages/home/key-documents (accessed 22 March 2009).

General Medical Council (2009a) *Medical Students: Professional Values and Fitness to Practise. Guidance from the GMC and the MSC.* http://www.gmc-uk.org/education/documents/GMC_Medical%20students.pdf (accessed 21 April 2009).

General Medical Council (2009b) *Tomorrow's Doctors*, rev edn. http://www.gmc-uk.org/tomorrowsdoctors (accessed 4 March 2009).

Ham, C. and Dickinson, H. (2007) *Engaging Doctors in Leadership: What Can We Learn from International Experience and Research Evidence.* NHS Institute for Innovation and Improvement.

Liker, J. (2004) *The Toyota Way: 14 Management Principles from the World's Greatest Manufacturer.* McGraw-Hill, New York.

Medical Schools Council (2006) *Guiding Principles for the Admission of Medical Students.* http://www.chms.ac.uk/documents/RevisedAdmprinciplesNov2006M-SCwording27.1.09.pdf (accessed 16 March 2009).

NHS Institute for Innovation and Improvement, Academy of Medical Royal Colleges (2008) *Medical Leadership Competency Framework*, 2nd edn. http://www.institute.nhs.uk/images/documents/MLCF%20May%202009.pdf (accessed 15 April 2009).

Postgraduate Medical Education and Training Board (2008) *Educating Tomorrow's Doctors – Future Models of Medical Training; Medical Workforce Shape and Trainee Expectations.* http://www.pmetb.org.uk/fileadmin/user/Content_and_Outcomes/Working_group_reports/Educating_Tomorrows_Doctors_working_group_report_20080620_v1.pdf (accessed 6 March 2009).

Spence, D. (2009) Comic leadership. *British Medical Journal*, **338**, 887.

CHAPTER 9

MBA or not?

Claire Woolcock

This chapter explores the value of doing an MBA (Masters in Business Administration).

Some clinicians, including doctors, may find the opportunity for more formal training in management appealing. The medical workforce includes some of the most intelligent, highly trained and motivated people in the NHS. Doctors' careers are likely to involve managing others, leading teams and setting up new services despite a lack of formal training in how to do this.

While the experience of shadowing, of leadership development programmes and of short courses is undoubtedly of value, there are a growing number of clinicians who have decided to pursue a more formal training in management or business. This is both to acquire knowledge about the running of an organisation and also a means of gaining credibility amongst their manager peers. A number of courses are now available which have been specifically tailored for management in the healthcare industry. Some clinicians may decide to study broader business degrees, such as doing an MBA or a Masters specifically in Healthcare Management.

These courses are costly in terms of personal finances, time and energy. Deciding whether to do such a course is not a decision to be made lightly. MBAs are not part of the qualification pathway of traditional clinical careers and so may feel foreign and uncertain. This chapter shares insights about the content of an MBA, describes how various courses differ, and reviews the challenges and benefits of completing such courses.

What is an MBA?

An MBA is a postgraduate university degree covering a broad range of subjects, leading to a generalist qualification in business studies, encompassing the range of functions and practices that make up a business. The course originated in American business schools in the early twentieth century, at a time when the country was industrialising and there was a need for a more scientific approach to business. MBAs spread to Europe in the 1950s and have since spread across the world to become the most popular postgraduate degree. In the USA, there are 90,000 MBA graduates annually and in the UK, over 10,000. The Association of MBAs currently accredits 157 programmes in 71 countries (Association of MBAs, 2009).

Once the domain of financiers, business schools now recognise that the skills taught in an MBA programme are transferable to many other industries. It is not uncommon for an MBA cohort to originate from a diverse range of industries, all high-achievers in their respective domains. In the USA, the acknowledgment of the benefits of an MBA has led to the rise of joint MBA programmes including joint MBA/LLB for lawyers and MBA/MD for doctors, such as the programme at Harvard. At present, there is no joint medical/MBA programme in the UK, as many business schools feel it beneficial for students to have worked in their respective industry for several years before undertaking an MBA. This enriches the class discussions as students can learn from sharing richer personal experiences. Each business school will have its own admission policy which will specify any minimum work experience or other criteria for admission.

A full-time MBA commonly takes one to two years of study. An executive MBA will take two to four years of part-time study. Executive MBA students tend to be older and more experienced, and often continue full-time employment alongside their MBA. For distance-learning MBAs, classes are carried out by correspondence or online, rather than on university campus.

Why do an MBA?

Unlike medicine, with its compulsory and formal training and accreditation, people with no formal training or qualifications hold many jobs in business. Business organisations employ people with diverse educational backgrounds. Some of the most successful and prominent business people, including Alan Sugar and Richard Branson, have no higher qualifications at all. Studying an MBA is one way of learning the basics of business and management and demonstrating a certain level of knowledge and skill.

By acquiring the theoretical basis for business and management, MBA graduates become more marketable. They acquire a 'brand' and often great networks as well as formally acquired transferable skills which will enable them to take on roles that might have otherwise have been beyond them. Clinicians with MBAs may or may not choose to continue working clinically after graduation.

Studying an MBA is challenging. Business studies are quite unlike clinical studies, which creates a refreshing challenge for the intellectually curious.

There are many examples of MBA graduates gaining promotion or pay rises after completing their MBA, and league tables of such exist comparing schools. Common as it is, it is by no means inevitable that everyone with an MBA receives an increase in their salary, and perhaps less likely in healthcare. This will depend on the industry and position in which you are working and on your personal choices about your career path following completion of an MBA. Bear in mind that an MBA is expensive, often funded out of pocket by the students themselves.

What will an MBA teach me?

All MBAs cover similar core courses. Different business schools have areas of specialty which enable them to offer bespoke courses such as health management or entrepreneurship. Just as the range of courses varies between schools, so do the quality and style of teaching.

The core curriculum generally includes the following areas. Accountancy involves an understanding of how to record, verify and report on financial statements about a business. Economics is the study of the production, distribution and consumption of goods and services. Finance is the study of managing money and risk. Strategic management is the study of drafting, implementing and evaluating decisions about how an organisation can achieve its aims. Marketing is the study of the planning, implementation and control of business activities to bring together buyers and sellers. Organisational behaviour is the study of how organisations and individuals within organisations behave. Examples of additional optional courses may include innovation, social enterprise and change management amongst many others, as well as courses exploring the topics above in greater depth.

Beyond the formal taught courses, an MBA also teaches other skills.

MBA programmes include significant project work to be completed by teams of students from diverse backgrounds with different experience and skills. These projects often involve working in a pressured environment with a tight deadline. Some business schools introduce a consultancy model, so the student cohort has an external client to whom they deliver a piece of work.

Whether doing the course part-time or full-time, there is a degree of constant pressure to learn a great deal of information and deliver high-quality coursework. If working full-time, there is the additional challenge of balancing the demands of employment alongside coursework and learning to prioritise work–life balance along the way.

Clinicians spend their careers focusing on their patients. Learning to manage and progress a project from the early stages of gathering information to the final delivery of a product over a number of months demands a different skill set that is core to management roles.

Studying an MBA inevitably leads to a greater understanding of how the overall global economy operates, as well as the individual organisation.

Where will an MBA lead to?

The traditional medical management career pathway, after Completion of Clinical Training (CCT), is to become a clinical director for a clinical department, and then to progress to medical director for a trust. As of April 2009, across the NHS there are 13 Chief Executives who are medically trained out of a total of more than 600 chief executives of NHS organisations (Carvel and Gentleman, 2009). There are many more medically trained Chief Executives in the USA. Whilst it is not essential to have a management qualification to progress along this career path, the knowledge and behaviours from an MBA would certainly be of benefit. In primary care, General Practitioners can progress to become medical directors or Chief Executives of Primary Care Trusts, or move into hospital leadership.

Without moving into a full-time management position, it is still possible for clinicians with MBAs to be involved in the management of their organisation, through project management, leading quality improvement, or service line management.

One of the risks of clinicians doing MBAs, for health systems, if not for individuals, is that often high-potential individuals will leave healthcare to work elsewhere. Most commonly, doctors move to work for the pharmaceutical industry. However, the skills acquired through clinical and management training are transferable to a broad range of industries and ultimately career paths depend on personal circumstance and preferences.

The NHS spent £350 million on management consultancy in 2008 to assist NHS organisations to develop services, manage projects and improve performance. Clinicians with MBAs are well placed for consultancy, having both business acumen and the healthcare experience to understand a complex industry.

The Department of Health and Strategic Health Authorities (SHA) employ clinicians to contribute to developing policy. Some of the skills learnt through an MBA may develop interest in this national tier and policy. This could be through a secondment as a Clinical Advisor or a more permanent change in career.

A small number of clinicians with MBAs choose to do further academic research in healthcare management, progressing on an academic career path, while others find MBAs equip them with the tools to become successful entrepreneurs.

Key questions to consider prior to doing an MBA

There is no way round the fact that studying for an MBA will absorb a considerable amount of your time. The degree of teamwork required for projects demands regular contact with other members of your team. This means that the course will occupy significantly more time than the teaching hours and private study you allocate.

One of the best ways to decide on the optimum time to do your MBA is to consider which stage of your career will allow you the most flexibility. There will undoubtedly be some stages in your career when you have more time than others; for example, starting an MBA prior to other professional exams or job interviews may be unwise. An MBA usually has the most impact and validity for the first year following graduation, so if you wish to use the MBA as an opportunity to change careers entirely, doing this as soon as possible following MBA graduation is the ideal.

Studying for an MBA will take one to two years and your circumstances may well change during that time. If you think that is likely, choosing a business school that allows for flexibility between part- and full-time and distant learning may be preferable.

The first question that anyone will ask an individual with an MBA is 'Where did you get your MBA from?'. This is because not all MBAs are the same and a business school's reputation or ranking is very important for the value of the MBA. Higher-performing business schools are able to charge considerably more for their MBA programmes, which are of more value to students, not only in the quality of the learning but also in terms of salary and job opportunities. An MBA from a lesser university may not be advisable for ambitious clinicians. An MBA currently costs in the region of £15,000 to £45,000 in tuition fees. The *Financial Times* ranks all MBA programmes, looking at several different factors including teaching, results and increase in salary post-MBA. Generally, the better courses cost more. As an MBA is likely to be one of the most expensive investments you will make, it is important to be sure that the investment will be worthwhile. In addition to the tuition fees, additional costs will include books, stationery and travel.

Many business schools have close links with industries and organisations which provide opportunities for networking and developing relationships during the course. All business schools offer coaching and career advice to facilitate setting up internships, introductions and interviews.

How to fund the MBA

Each individual's ability to fund an MBA will differ. The financial commitment involved frequently delays clinicians who plan to study an MBA. The earlier you start to think about the finances and try to save for this, the better. Some clinicians undertake additional locum work to contribute towards tuition fees. The sacrifices you are willing to make in the short term will be dictated by the value you envisage an MBA bringing to your longer term career success.

Loan schemes are available from high street banks (e.g. NatWest) for MBAs. This enables the cost of the course to be spread over several years and will hopefully become more affordable as your career progresses.

Most clinicians in training are currently entitled to a study leave budget from the local deanery which can be used to contribute towards tuition fees. Although this is very unlikely to cover the full cost, there are occasionally additional funds that can be used to fund higher degrees, at the discretion of the budget holder. It is therefore always worth being bold and directly asking your trust and Strategic Health Authority whether there is any budget available to contribute towards leadership development such as would be gained through an MBA.

A number of organisations and charities have grants available to fund training and higher education. If you are considering studying abroad, the Rotary Club has scholarships available.

As the value of understanding business and management principles for effective clinical leadership is increasingly recognised, it is hoped that funding becomes increasingly accessible for doctors. Many businesses see sufficient value in MBAs that they sponsor employees to do an MBA (albeit with a commitment to remain working for the company for some time following graduation).

Alternative management training

An MBA is valuable but expensive and excessive to the requirements of the majority of clinicians who take on management roles. Below is a selection of alternative management training options.

Clinicians often attend management training courses prior to consultant interviews. This is because management is a common area of questions for interviews. Clinicians are now expected to have an understanding of the structure of healthcare organisations, and an overview of what is involved in running them. This has become more relevant with the evolution of Foundation

Trusts and commissioning described in Part 1 of this book. Doctors reaching their CCT are often encouraged to attend short management courses run by their trust, SHA or other organisation such as the Kings Fund. These courses aim to develop personal leadership skills and increase knowledge regarding the structures and systems within the NHS.

There are a number of private companies that specialise in providing management training. These are often expensive, but can be particularly beneficial in developing the 'soft skills' of management and leadership, including time management, delegation and presentation skills. Some of these skills are covered in the following chapter.

BAMM (British Association of Medical Managers) runs development programmes for doctors. 'Fit to Lead' is a course for consultants and doctors who hold management positions. BAMM is currently developing programmes for medical students and junior doctors. Fit to Lead combines skills training with a personalised development programme assessing the expertise gained over a year. BAMMbino, for junior doctors, runs free events across the country catering for junior doctors with an interest in management.

There are a growing number of universities offering a Masters (MSc) in healthcare or medical management. These programmes have been specifically designed with the healthcare industry in mind, but vary in terms of their applicability. As with an MBA, it pays to examine the suitability of any programme carefully before committing to it (although the cost of such courses is significantly less than a typical MBA, in the region of £5,000 to £15,000).

Another alternative to a training course is to get practical experience as a manager through a secondment or permanent move to working in industry. Rather than learning about business and management in an academic environment, here clinicians learn about management by actually doing it. Though few currently do so, the learning is particularly rich and real.

There is a wide array of choices regarding whether to study an MBA or a Masters, or to gain practical hands-on management experience through local projects or a placement in industry. The decision depends on both personal circumstances and individual preferences. The goal for any of these options must be to equip clinical leaders with the skills and confidence to deliver real and sustainable improvements in the quality and efficiency of care that patients receive.

References and further reading

Association of MBAs (2009) http://www.mbaworld.com/MBAWorld/index.jsp (accessed 30 May 2009).

BAMM (2009) BAMMbino. http://www.bamm.co.uk/Services/Support_%26_Development/BAMMbino_2007072440/ (accessed 5 June 2009).

Carvel, J. and Gentleman, A. (2009) Cold shouldered. The *Guardian*, 14 January. http://www.guardian.co.uk/society/2009/jan/14/nhs-equality-health-public-sector-careers (accessed 15 June 2009).

Financial Times (2009) *Global MBA Rankings 2009*. http://rankings.ft.com/businessschoolrankings/global-mba-rankings (accessed 25 May 2009).

Harvard Business School (2009) Harvard Business School Joint Degree Programmes. http://www.hbs.edu/mba/academics/mppmba.html (accessed 25 May 2009).

NatWest (2009) MBA loan. http://www.natwest.com/personal/loans/g1/professional-training-loan/mba.ashx (accessed 1 June 2009).

Rotary (2009) Ambassadorial scholarships. http://www.rotary.org/en/studentsandyouth/educationalprograms/ambassadorialscholarships/Pages/ridefault.aspx (accessed 20 May 2009).

Staines, R. (2009) NHS spent £350m on consultants in the last year, claims survey. *Nursing Times*, 10 May. http://www.nursingtimes.net/whats-new-in-nursing/rcn-congress/nhs-spent-350m-on-consultants-in-the-last-year-claims-survey/5001275.article (accessed 20 May 2009).

PART 3

Practical tips for clinicians

Part 3 covers a range of practical skills to act as a 'starter kit' for the aspiring clinical leader. Of course it is not comprehensive (not all practical skills needed are covered), and readers may wish to delve in more detail into those that are covered. In addition to advice on leadership development through mentoring, presentations and chairing meetings, this section also covers the less familiar topics of how to resolve conflict through negotiation: something we all do day to day, but typically receive little or no formal training in. The final chapter in this section is about becoming a clinical leader not in the NHS, but on a wider stage addressing the challenges of global health.

Malcolm Gladwell's book *Outliers* (2008) discusses some secrets for success for those aspiring to be leaders in their fields. In addition to the opportunities presented through chance, Gladwell explains that it is not simply what you do on a single occasion that will make you stand out as being successful, but additionally the amount of effort, training and development that you put in and receive over many years. While Gladwell, and a whole body of literature, fully recognise that innate talent is important, the evidence equally shows that it is not sufficient to be 'born' to lead. You also have to make yourself into a leader through focus, effort and experience.

This book signposts the reader to a variety of exciting opportunities and routes to acquire the skills and experience required to make readers into effective clinical leaders. Armed with this information, it is now up to you to carve out the most appropriate career path to build on your passions and to develop your strengths and interests.

The 'Generation Y' approach to careers (Asthana, 2008) is likely to be fundamentally different from that of their parents, the 'Baby Boomers'. Generation Y (born between 1982 and 2002 and alternatively known as the 'internet generation') are much less likely to have one job for life. To generalise: Generation Y prioritise flexible working, travel and a better work–life balance over security and salary. How this will impact healthcare systems, and how systems should respond to ensure their workforce needs are met, is unclear. But it seems likely that increasing numbers of aspiring clinical leaders will be bolder and more creative with their career paths: research suggests that Generation Y are far more willing to challenge authority and convention and are less deterred by traditional hierarchies. This suggests we can be optimistic that a generation of future clinical leaders is coming through which will be courageous enough to break the mould in service of causes about which they are passionate. Today's senior leaders need to identify and nurture this up-and-coming talent, harnessing its energy to the benefit of patients and populations in the UK and globally.

References and further reading

Asthana, A. (2008) Generation Y: They don't live for work…they work to live. *The Observer*, 25 May.

Gladwell, M. (2008) *Outliers: The Story of Success*. Penguin, London.

CHAPTER 10

Survival skills for leadership

Daniel Richard Leff and Penny Humphris

As this book demonstrates, emerging clinical leaders need to focus on developing excellent leadership skills alongside excellent clinical skills throughout their training. Preceding chapters have introduced the reader to a wide range of opportunities available to develop these skills. Despite the recent update of the GMC Tomorrow's Doctors programme, there is currently no systematic programme in place to develop leadership skills as part of the core UK medical undergraduate or postgraduate curriculum.

Naturally, it is not possible to cover all aspects of personal development in one book. This chapter introduces the reader to an overview of the (survival) skills-based model of leadership, including practical tips on leadership skills such as chairing meetings and presentation skills. Chapter 11 deals specifically with conflict resolution and negotiation.

Defining leadership skills

Whilst leadership itself may be transparent and easy to recognise, leadership skills are much harder to define or conceptualise. If the definition of leadership is the art of motivating and directing a group of people to achieve a common goal (as discussed in the Introduction), then it follows that leadership skills are the capabilities of the leader that make others want to follow that direction. Leaders require the external skills to inspire others as well as the inner skills to lead themselves. Here we define leadership skills as the ability to use one's knowledge and competencies to accomplish a set of goals or objectives. Leadership can be considered purely from a *'skills perspective'*, stressing the knowledge and skills that make effective leadership possible. Figure 10.1 illustrates three basic skill sets – technical, human and conceptual – that are common to all leaders, and that can be developed and cultivated. These skills, defined by Katz (1974), are viewed as distinct from traits or innate qualities of

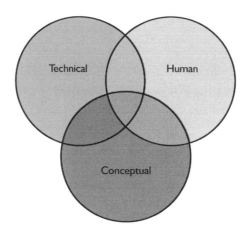

Figure 10.1 The fundamental skill sets of a good leader (Katz, 1974).

leaders. Skills imply what leaders can accomplish, whereas traits imply who leaders are, their 'innate characteristics'. Therefore leadership skills must be acquired by identifying, learning and honing them through practice, as discussed in Chapter 7.

Technical skills refer to specific knowledge about and proficiency in a certain type of work and activity. It requires competencies in a specialised area, analytical ability and ability to use certain tools and techniques. Examples of technical skills include health strategy development or minimally invasive surgery.

Human skills are those personal and people skills necessary for effective team leadership and working (as discussed in Chapter 4). These are distinct from technical skills, which are working with 'things' as opposed to people. People skills enable a leader both to understand themselves and to work with others to achieve goals. This includes the ability to be self-aware about the impact one has on others and to understand the perspectives of others. A leader with strong human skills will take others into account and will be empathetic to the feelings of those around them. For a clinical leader this means being able to relate equally well to patients, their families and to colleagues (both clinicians and others) at all levels.

The concept of emotional intelligence, as described by Daniel Goleman, describes our ability to make sense of our emotions both within ourselves and between ourselves and others. Goleman identifies five elements of emotional intelligence that are crucial to leaders:

■ *Self-awareness*, which includes 'knowing thyself' – having a deep understanding of yourself.

- *Self-regulation*, being able to control your impulses, to know how you feel about something but to be able not to act it out semi- or unconsciously.
- *Motivation*, having the self-motivation to achieve, from an inner sense of commitment and engagement with the work, task and people.
- *Empathy*, meaning the ability to put yourself in the shoes of the other person, being sensitive and thoughtful about the feelings of others.
- *Social skills*, such as friendliness with a purpose, social grace, confidence and interest in others.

The ability to understand and motivate others begins with the ability to know and manage oneself. Self-awareness is an essential underpinning of effective leadership behaviours. Many diagnostic tools for assessing leadership skills and qualities identify the individual's strengths and weaknesses in these areas and consider their impact on others, as discussed with the case study in Chapter 5.

Emotional intelligence can be learned and developed, but it takes time and commitment and will not happen without a genuine desire to change and a concerted effort on the part of the individual.

Conceptual skills represent the ability to work with ideas and concepts. A leader with conceptual skills is comfortable talking about the ideas that shape an organisation and the complexities involved. This type of leader is capable of expressing and clearly articulating the goals of the organisation in a way that others can comprehend and apply to their own situations. For the clinical leader, conceptual skills refer to the ability to understand and contribute to the policies, strategies and goals of the NHS nationally and locally and to initiate events that bring about improvements in people's health and in organisations involved in healthcare.

Following on from the work conducted by Katz in the mid-1950s, Mumford *et al.* formulated a skills-based model of leadership by examining the relationship between the leader's knowledge, skills and performance. The skills model of leadership is illustrated in Figure 10.2. Rather than describing what leaders do, the skills approach frames leadership as the capabilities that make effective leadership possible. There are five different components to the skills-based model: competencies, individual attributes, leadership outcomes, career experiences and environmental influences. We will consider each of these components in turn.

Competencies

Competencies for effective leadership include problem-solving skills, social judgement, and knowledge.

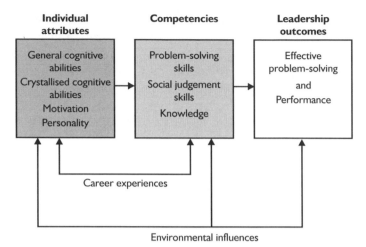

Figure 10.2 A skills-based model of leadership. Adapted from Mumford *et al.* (2000a,b).

- *Problem-solving skills* include the leader's creative ability to solve new, unusual and ill-defined organisational problems, gather information, formulate new understandings about the problem and to generate prototype plans for solutions.
- *Social judgment skills* are the capacity to understand people and social systems. The concept of social judgment can be subdivided as follows:
  - *Perspective taking* means understanding the attitudes that others may hold toward a particular problem or solution. This is empathy applied to problem solving.
  - *Social perceptiveness* means having both insight and awareness regarding how others within the organisation function. Ask yourself the following questions: What is important to others? What motivates *them*? What problems do they face and how will they react to change? A leader with social perceptiveness has a sense of how employees will respond to proposed change within the organisation.
  - *Behavioural flexibility* is the capacity to change and adapt one's behaviour in the light of understanding others' perspectives. It is important to maintain openness and desire to change. This capability will assist a leader to adapt to new demands following situational change.
  - *Social performance* is the ability of a leader to articulate and communicate a clear vision to others. This is especially important in circumstances of resistance to change and interpersonal conflict. In case of the latter, a good leader will act as a mediator and assist conflict resolution, which is discussed in the following chapter.

■ *Knowledge* has a positive impact on the ability of leaders to define complex organisational problems and to attempt solutions. For today's clinical leader, knowledge is not simply about having an extensive list of facts about the NHS. Rather, it is about the accumulation of relevant information and the ability to organise and apply it in an appropriate way.

Individual attributes

The individual attributes that have an impact on leadership skills and knowledge include: general cognitive ability, crystallised cognitive ability, motivation and personality.

■ *General cognitive ability* is an individual's intelligence. This includes information processing, perceptual processing, general reasoning skills, creative and divergent thinking skills and memory skills. Intelligence has a positive impact on both a leader's acquisition of complex problem-solving skills and their overall knowledge.
■ *Crystallised cognitive ability* is a form of intellectual ability that is learned or acquired over time. It is knowledge acquired through experience. It includes the ability to comprehend complex information and learn new skills. This type of acquired intelligence is relatively stable and does not decline with age.
■ *Motivation* indicates willingness: leaders need to be proactive, seeking to influence a situation and then show willing to tackle complex organisational problems. For leadership to occur, a person must firstly want to lead and then be willing to exert their influence.

Finally, *personality* traits undoubtedly play a role in leadership development. For example, charisma is a common trait of many successful leaders (see Chapter 5).

Leadership outcomes

Effective problem-solving by creating solutions that are logical and effective and can be implemented, and performance (the measures of how well a leader has done their job) together represent the outcomes of leadership as measured using the skills-based model discussed above.

Career experiences and environmental influences

Experiences gathered during the leader's career will influence their knowledge and skills. Leadership can be developed through challenging job assignments, mentoring, appropriate training, and hands-on experience in solving new and unusual problems. This means that leaders are shaped by their experiences and are not necessarily 'born' to be leaders. Finally, environmental factors that are outside a leader's competencies, characteristics and experiences may also have an influence. For example, if a problem is especially complex or the external context changes, the leader's performance may be affected.

To summarise the skills approach to leadership: this framework appears rather complex, but the crux of the theory is simple. It holds that leadership skills come with practice and refinement, rather than being innate. The key is to commit oneself to practising these skills in everyday settings, and to continually evaluate the outcomes and methods for improving effectiveness in every scenario. When joining committees, task forces, or work streams, consider each one a learning exercise as well as providing the opportunity to contribute to the debate and discussion. Ask yourself the following questions: What skills are being used here? What skills are working well? Which skills do I need to develop? Certain leadership skills will be harnessed by their use in specific settings such as when delivering presentations, chairing meetings, managing organisational change and resolving conflicts. These skills will be discussed in more detail in the next section.

Stress

Managing stress is a critical skill for aspiring leaders to master. Change can be stressful and the effective clinical leader needs to be able to manage their own stress in addition to the stress of those around them. Some common mistakes in dealing with organisational change and stress are as follows:

- Assuming that caring management will keep stress in the workplace to a minimum. This is not necessarily true and is not guaranteed to get the best results.
- Wasting time and energy attempting to influence factors that are beyond your control. When the inevitable is resisted, stress and frustration will increase. The rate of change occurring within the NHS cannot be controlled; therefore it is preferable to keep up with the organisation's intended rate of change.

■ Holding on to priorities which are no longer relevant to the current situation. In order to take on new duties, old duties must be relinquished. Issues that previously had significance may no longer seem important. When wanting to do things right it is easy to fall into the trap of not doing the right things.

■ Failing to prioritise in an environment with many potential issues of conflict and causes asking for support. Some battles may not be worth fighting. One approach is to ask: 'Will this issue be important five years from now?'. Identify battles that are big enough to matter, yet small enough to win, with reasonable effort.

■ Shying away from unfamiliar duties. This is a short-sighted strategy that may create bigger problems in the future, since typically this delays the point at which you are forced to take on the new role or responsibility.

In summary, stress and change are integral parts of healthcare organisations today, just as they are for organisations outside healthcare. Good clinical leaders have found ways to cope with both, and even to use them to achieve the organisation's objectives.

Chairing

Meetings are important and an essential part of clinical practice as well as for management roles. They provide a forum for discussion and decision-making, for planning and monitoring organisational change. Unfocused and unproductive meetings are a waste of everyone's time. Formal discussions require focus and direction to prevent them from becoming social 'chit chat' or isolated foci of discord and disagreement. However, open debate requires stewardship to enable all views to be heard and conclusions based upon reasoned argument, consensus or compromise. This is the role of the chairperson or *chair*.

Chairing provides an excellent opportunity for developing communication and leadership skills. The characteristics of effective chairing are:

■ *Clear leadership* with a clear purpose and desired end-point for the meeting, providing a direction and framework for debate and working within specific ground rules.

■ *Focusing and balancing debates* by allowing everyone a chance to express their views.

■ *Ensuring a decision is reached* by agreeing an outcome that all members accept (even if unanimous agreement cannot be reached).

- *Building a sense of teamworking* by allowing people to build rapport and to make contributions.
- *Saving time and energy* by being efficient and timely.

Chairs have to be very well prepared to be effective. It is imperative they know the issues and topics well for discussion, including their background. Good chairs will invest time getting to know other members of the group, to understand their personalities and to identify who helps and who hinders their role.

Preparing thoroughly by reading all the background papers, understanding the agenda and objectives of each item and planning strategies for running the meeting helps a chair to focus on timekeeping and encouraging productive discussions.

Some more detailed tips on the mechanics of chairing are provided in Table 10.1.

One of the most difficult challenges whilst chairing a meeting is encouraging participation and prompting discussion. The following tips may be helpful to encourage participation from all attendees:

- Ask open and searching questions by probing, testing and challenging others to get to the crux of the problem or issue being discussed.
- Use active listening through the use of body language such as nodding, eye contact, and smiling.

Table 10.1 The mechanics of chairing a meeting.

Before the meeting	During the meeting	After the meeting
Clarify the meeting's objectives	Establish ground rules	Recap key points, decisions and actions (who will do what, and by when)
Ensure the correct people attend	Clarify roles and responsibilities	Agree agenda for the next meeting
Check your seating position: the venue, the layout, the audiovisuals	Gain commitment to the agenda: 'Today we must achieve, x, y and z'	Thank all participants for the contribution
Have contingency for non-attendance of members	Steer discussions in a structured fashion	Ensure the meeting notes (minutes) reflect key agreements, facts or quotes
Prepare for the meeting: read the background, know the agenda	Encourage a wide range of views and opinions	Ensure progress on agreed action points
	Try to summarise at key moments	
	Keep discussion to time	

- Employ soft commands, such as responses that sound like questions to elicit information. For example, 'Perhaps you could explain', or 'Perhaps you could expand'.
- Pay attention to those who look like they wish to be brought into the debate and acknowledge them.

Finally, success for the meeting will depend upon reaching and presenting decisions that are SMART (specific, measurable, action-orientated, realistic and time-limited; see Table 10.2), and on someone taking and circulating notes at the appropriate level of detail. Often, a brief summary of actions by whom and by when is enough.

Table 10.2 Guidelines on SMART recommendations.

Specific – clear about what is required and the evidence to support the recommendation

Measurable – capable of being monitored and thereby enabling success or failure determined

Action-orientated – focused on what needs to be achieved

Realistic – grounded, within the limits of the resources (such as staffing or finances)

Time-limited – set within clear deadlines, milestones and timetables for action

Presentation skills

Presentations are a valuable method for communicating ideas and goals to a group. Done well, presentations can also be ways to show personality, humour and humility. The presenter's style can help stimulate immediate discussion and debate. However, for many people, preparing and delivering oral presentations induces considerable stress. In this section we review the content of a good presentation, and provide some tips to minimise the stress of talking to groups of people.

A good presentation will have both useful content and a logical and coherent structure. There is no quick alternative to investing time in planning, preparing and practising the presentation in advance.

Good speakers have control over their voice. The skill here is to use the different facets or attributes of your voice to help people take away as much information as possible. For example, lowering your voice can draw the audience in, whilst raising it can emphasise an important point. If the tone of your voice carries laughter, you are more likely to leave the audience smiling and more inclined to remember what you said. Varying the pace will help to keep the audience interested. In general, it is better to speak slowly so that people have the best chance of hearing you. It can be useful to record yourself and listen to the tape before you present an important talk. This will help you to understand the way you are using the different attributes of your voice and assess whether you are speaking too quickly.

Use your body language to good effect and engage the audience through eye contact. Using positive facial expressions such as smiling will help the audience see you as friendly and more approachable. This will make them want to listen to you more and makes them more likely to ask questions. Using hand gestures may facilitate understanding and capture attention. Standing upright and leaning forward implies confidence. Avoid standing too far away and positioning yourself to one side of an audience. It may be preferable to move from side to side throughout the talk although some speakers prefer to stand still. If you have visuals, do not stand between them and the audience – talk to the audience, not to the screen. The authors have found it useful to practise in front of a mirror to visualise their body language and to iron out their own idiosyncratic habits in communication.

When people ask questions, try to use active listening. It is best to avoid finishing people's sentences and to avoid answering questions with questions. Try also to avoid dominating the exchange, and let the other speaker be heard and understood. This is especially important if there are conflicting points of view. It may be helpful to use non-verbal communication to acknowledge a point of view. The use of eye contact and head nodding can be very powerful. Before responding, it is often sensible to paraphrase questions to be sure you have understood (for example, 'This is what I understand from what you have just said... am I correct?'), which also buys you a little time to think. When responding to questions, respond to the whole audience, not just the questioner, as this will keep everyone focused on the discussion. If you disagree with a view, it may be wise first to acknowledge the other's point of view (for example, 'There is a lot to be said for that, but...'). It is important to ensure that disagreements do not lead to tension within the audience or make people feel uncomfortable.

The following tips outlined by Orman (2002) may be useful if you have anxiety about presenting:

1. *Speaking is not inherently stressful.* Human beings speak in public all the time in diverse situations. You are no less human than anyone else, and like them you can overcome any fears of speaking in public.
2. *You don't have to be brilliant or perfect to succeed.* The audience does not expect a perfect performance, but wants something of value, so give them that and you will be considered a success.

3. *All you need is two to three main points.* People are likely to remember only a few facts from your talk. Think about what your main points are and make sure people come away with those in mind. This will avoid any unnecessary over-complexity, and will make your job as a speaker more entertaining for both you and the audience. People tend to remember most what you open and close with, so ensure your main messages are either at the start or the end of your talk, or both.

4. *You need a purpose that is right for the task.* Your purpose is not to get everyone in the room to agree with you. Whether you do a great job or not, there will always be people who do not approve of either you or your argument. It is human nature that in any large group there will be differences of opinion and judgment. Remember that your purpose as a speaker is to *give*, not to get.

5. *To succeed, do not consider yourself a 'public speaker'.* It is more important to be yourself. Do not strive to emulate the qualities or style of 'public speakers'. Instead, use the skills you already have. This will liberate you to be yourself and make you a far more effective communicator in public.

6. *Humility and humour go a long way.* Humour is a common language, so if it feels natural for you then go for it. Humility means standing in front of others and sharing some of your own frailties, weaknesses and mistakes. Being humble can make you more credible, believable and (paradoxically) more respected. Using both humour and humility, by telling amusing stories to demonstrate your own personal failings can be both illuminating and entertaining.

7. *When you speak in public, nothing 'bad' is likely to happen.* Simply, there is nothing awful that will come from you talking in public.

8. *Don't try to control the behaviour of the audience.* Do not worry if people are fidgeting or appear restless. Instead, stay in control and keep going.

9. *Don't be over-prepared.* There is a fine line between being well-prepared and over-preparing. Over-preparing makes you less effective, since it removes your spontaneity, and your personality will shine through less.

10. *Your audience wants you to succeed.* In general, the audience is on your side. An incorrect phrase that doesn't match exactly how you practised it may seem a big deal for you, but it matters little to the audience (who may well not even notice it). Remind yourself of this point, especially if you feel you have performed poorly.

In summary, aspiring clinical leaders need to be able to combine high-quality clinical care with management and leadership responsibilities. This chapter has outlined a skills-based model of clinical leadership and focused on practical tips for improving your communication through chairing meetings and presenting. To blossom as a leader, you must communicate well.

References and further reading

Davidhizar, R. (1998) Surviving organisational change. In: E. C. Hein (ed.) *Contemporary Leadership Behaviors*. Lippincott, New York.

DiStefano, J. and Masnevski, M. L, (1996) Process and performance in multicultural teams. *Harvard Business Review*, **3**, 10.

General Medical Council (2009) *Tomorrow's Doctors*. http://www.gmc-uk.org/education/undergraduate/undergraduate_policy/tomorrows_doctors.asp (accessed 3 April 2009).

Goldstein, A. O. *et al.* (2009) Teaching Advanced Leadership Skills in Community Service (ALSCS) to medical students. *Academic Medicine*, **84**(6), 754–64.

Goleman, D. (1996) *Emotional Intelligence: Why it Can Matter More Than IQ*. Bloomsbury, London.

Katz, J. W. (1974) Skills of an effective administrator. *Harvard Business Review*, **52**, 90–102.

Mumford, M. D., Zaccaro, S. J., Connelly, M. S. and Marks, M. A. (2000a) Leadership skills: conclusions and future directions *Leadership Quarterly*, **11**(1), 155–70.

Mumford, M. D., Zaccaro, S. J., Harding, F. D., Jacobs, T. O. and Fleishman, E. A. (2000b) Leadership skills for a changing world: solving complex social problems. *Leadership Quarterly*, **11**(1), 23.

Northouse, P. (2004) *Leadership: Theory and Practice*, 3rd edn. Sage Publications, California.

Orman, M. C. (2002) How to conquer public speaking fear. http://www.stresscure.com/jobstress/speak.html (accessed 7 May 2009).

Porter-O'Grady, T. (1998) The seven basic rules for successful redesign. In: E. C. Hein (ed.) *Contemporary Leadership Behaviors*. Lippincott, New York.

Spencer, S. A. and Adams, J. D. (1990) *Life Changes: Growing through Personal Transitions*. Impact Publishers, Atascadero, CA.

Umiker, W. (1998) Collaborative conflict resolution. In: E. C. Hein (ed.) *Contemporary Leadership Behaviors*. Lippincott, New York.

Zaccaro, S. J., Mumford, M. D., Connelly, M. S., Marks, M. A. and Gilbert, J. A. (2000) Assessment of leader problem-solving capabilities. *Leadership Quarterly*, **11**(1), 37–64.

CHAPTER 11

Conflict resolution and negotiation for leadership

Priya Agrawal and Leonard Marcus

For all leaders, the ability to recognise the potential for conflict and the skills to resolve it are vital to the smooth running and success of the organisation.

For both clinicians and managers, conflict is an unavoidable part of the job. CEOs in healthcare organisations often enter and exit through a fast-revolving door. The high turnover of senior managers and leaders that are experienced and talented is often a loss to organisations in many ways. Conflict is cited by many as one of the three main reasons for this regular movement of CEOs (the other two reasons are lack of mutual respect or trust among senior colleagues, and a clash of management styles) (Spurgeon, 2001). As has been previously discussed, individuals are often promoted to leadership positions in recognition of their clinical or technical skills rather than their management or leadership expertise or their ability to handle conflict. Although some leaders seek to avoid conflict at all costs, well-managed conflict can also bring positive results, such as identifying problems that need to be addressed, inspiring creative thinking or relieving otherwise distracting tensions and stress.

There are many opportunities for potential conflict:

- As a CEO you are responsible for leading change, the speed of which must keep pace with other social and economic shifts. Change is often associated with conflict, as when established policies and procedures are disrupted and a wave of discomfort is generated. The emotions and conflict that this generates requires careful managing.
- For a healthcare organisation to prosper it must itself be financially healthy, which can conflict with the organisation's clinical and societal mission. Leaders must manage this balance between clinical priorities and financial requirements.
- One of the challenges for clinicians who take on leadership roles is renegotiating working relationships with their clinical colleagues. This change

and dynamic can impose a 'them and us' divide between clinical leaders and others who had been their peers. Misunderstandings may arise between the new professional relationships, with disappointment or even jealousy being engendered.

■ When roles and responsibilities among colleagues and departments are not clear, the ambiguities naturally lead to conflict. This is most likely to occur when new leadership joins an organisation or department, when reorganisation occurs or when a department is asked to assume new responsibilities.

■ When different stakeholders view a problem or incident from differing perspectives, they are likely to interpret what took place in ways that are self-affirming. This can set up competing versions of the same story, and with that, conflict about what occurred and the implications of what occurred.

Conflict that is unresolved and poorly managed is a costly factor for healthcare organisations. When allowed to fester, it consumes the valuable time of both clinicians and managers, distracts from decision-making and, at worst, can lead to costly litigation. Conflict not managed well also restricts the opportunity to make differences of opinion and perspective an asset for those working together. Those differences when productively brought to the table can broaden the scope of experience and range of variables considered when reaching complex decisions.

To move towards resolution, the spiral of conflict escalation must be interrupted. Below are a set of recommendations to assist in this process:

1. *Accept that there will be conflict* – acknowledge it as inevitable and develop strategies to resolve and manage it. If possible, use it as an asset rather than a problem.
2. *Recognise the consequences of conflict* – ignoring or avoiding conflict can lead to compromised quality of care as important information may be missed and people can engage in a dangerous blame game.
3. *Clarify motive* – to reach a productive resolution, all parties must declare (at least to some degree) what it is they regard as success. Each party must give something of value in order to get something in return.
4. *Begin the learning process* – once a conflict is successfully resolved, those involved will often comment that they have learned something along the way. This could be about the motives of others, information critical to the decision or options that were otherwise not apparent. Adopting an openness to learning is most likely to lead to a mutually satisfying solution.
5. *Find the logic* – is there any validity to what the other party is saying? Ury (1993) suggests 'going to the balcony' to gain an understanding of the other's perspective from a distance.
6. *Understand the options* – there are more possibilities than simply 'winning' or 'losing'. Together, options need to be generated and considered in

order to find common ground and mutually satisfying solutions. Imagine what could be the positive returns of working together.

7. *Find common purpose* – it is easier to create common solutions if you can find a common interest. For example, what is in the patients' best interests could be a theme that motivates the search for common ground.

8. *Anticipate conflict* – to prepare for conflict you need to recognise it as a possibility. For example, those who work together on potentially divisive issues could be trained together on conflict resolution methods and techniques to be deployed when conflict arises. Having a shared strategy, vocabulary and framework can shift the focus from the process to the issues.

9. *Move beyond the conflict* – it is not easy to find common ground among people caught in conflict. This requires developing creative solutions based on common interests and purpose, such as the overarching goal of delivering high-quality healthcare.

Mastering the art of healthcare negotiation and conflict resolution is a topic of many books, courses and seminars; what follows is necessarily a brief overview.

Negotiation broadly can be defined as a two-way communication and decision-making process between parties aimed at reaching an agreement or solution to a shared problem. It occurs when each of the parties has some authority in making the decision, each has something at stake and each will be affected by the outcome. Negotiation is an everyday experience: in your personal life, you do it with your spouse to arrange childcare when one's on-call commitments conflict with the other's personal obligations. When you arrive at work you beg to be allowed into the car park without your identification badge, which has been misplaced at home. On the ward round, you spend time trying to convince a patient to comply with the physiotherapy regime to ensure better post-surgical recovery. Then you need to plead with the theatre sister to add another patient to the operating list, arguing that it will not cause it to over-run. Later, you attend a meeting where make your case to the financially challenged surgical board to commission new equipment for theatre. Although the risks and consequences of each scenario may differ, whether it is a formal negotiation at work or an informal discussion to get something you want from someone else, negotiation shapes our working and personal lives.

For healthcare professionals, facing high stakes in patient care as well as for career progression, the opportunity is ripe for these discussions to escalate into conflict. Time is limited, budgets are tight and there are multiple personalities and 'tribes' with different priorities. A successful leader can navigate this terrain simultaneously achieving those things which they regard as most important to them (positional bargaining) and fostering a situation in which all parties find value adding in the process and outcome (collaborative negotiation).

Positional bargaining

The term 'negotiation' usually conjures up images of big boardrooms haggling over a multi-million dollar contract or a tense phone call responding to a ransom demand in a hostage situation – these are examples of *positional bargaining*. Negotiation with a healthy exchange of information and perspective is always beneficial, but it may not always be possible. In situations where you are negotiating with someone who is a 'bully' or in circumstances (such as competition for funding) where there will undeniably be a winner and a loser, it is best to recognise the situation and play to win.

The defining characteristic of positional bargaining is that one party gains at the expense of the other. Positional bargaining involves opposing camps speaking different languages (for example, doctors speaking 'doctor', managers speaking 'manager') playing a win–lose game. Interests are subordinated to positions and flexibility is considered a weakness.

Winning requires the creation of leverage, which allows preferences to be imposed on the outcome of the negotiation. Leverage is the result of power, which comes by position, the development of allies to support you, data that proves your case or the creation of consequences that the other side wish to avoid, such as public disclosure. Positional bargaining can be dangerous in clinical settings and should be avoided when possible.

Collaborative negotiation

By contrast, collaborative problem-solving has the potential to be value-added for all parties to a negotiation. This approach recognises differences between the two parties as assets in the effort to discover solutions not previously considered. This is accomplished by placing shared interests and values on the table, developing a common purpose and by being flexible and open to new ideas.

A classic example of value-added negotiation is that of two individuals fighting over who is entitled to the one orange they must share. The seemingly fairest way to share it would be to divide the orange in half. However, by engaging each other's interests and what they most value they learn that for their separate purposes, one wants the inside of the orange for its juice and the other wants the rind on the outside. In discovering this solution, neither gives away anything of real value to them, while each receives more of what they want. Thus both are winners. The provision of healthcare offers many opportunities to apply this metaphor, both to patient care and organisational management.

Another example of collaborative negotiation is the division of housework. If one partner enjoys cooking and the other prefers cleaning, rather than each doing half of both tasks because it 'seems fair', there is an obvious 'gain–gain' solution.

In healthcare, the quality of patient care can be the perceived 'currency' for making decisions that forge shared purpose. This common interest, centred on the patient, ideally supersedes other factors such as participants' ego, relative power, turf or rank. The key question in decision-making and conflict resolution for all parties can be: 'Will this lead to optimal care for the patient?'.

Understanding what matters to each party is at the core of *interest-based negotiation*. Two key questions frame the method. First, what are each of the stakeholders to the negotiation hoping to accomplish? Second, how can we best work together to achieve a mutually beneficial outcome? The discussion that follows encourages everyone to explore their interests while they discover those of others. To reach a mutually beneficial solution, your most effective negotiation tool is a good question, and your most important asset is an imagination that explores a wide range of possibilities.

Preparation

> Most negotiations are won or lost even before the talking begins, depending on the quality of the preparation
>
> *William Ury, 1993*

Thorough preparation and investigative work leads to easier negotiation and greater success. An effective negotiator prepares in advance by anticipating and practising what to say and do in situations as they unfold. Ask yourself the following questions:

■ *What do you want and what are you prepared to offer/give? What are your genuine interests and motives?*
For example, is your real concern that primary care will not be able to care for your patient if discharged early, or is it that you want to prove your superiority? (Is it about one-upmanship?) Is it really that you think the radiologists will not be able to do as good a job as the surgeons, or are you worried about reducing your numbers? (Is it about territory?)
■ *What are the interests and motives of the other party?*
To modify or influence their thinking, you need to understand their thinking. Put yourself in their shoes and see the problem from their perspective.

What they value may be different from what you value. Emotions play an important role and can trump logic and rational explanation. For example, when negotiating about office locations, one person may care more about size and natural light, while another may care more about proximity to the department head or the kitchen. This can be an opportunity to apply the lesson of the divided orange.

■ *What possible solutions can you generate that would satisfy both sets of interests?*
Knowing the interests of both sides, brainstorm to stimulate the imaginative process and create options that will satisfy both interests. Do not evaluate the options until the brainstorming process is over, as this will stop the flow of creative thought. The possibility to combine disparate ideas to generate new ideas can be effective and attractive for both sides.

■ *What is my Best Alternative To a Negotiated Agreement (BATNA)?*
This is how you satisfy your interests without reaching an agreement. It is important to know when you have no choice but to leave the table. It may be possible to do so and still gain what you hope to achieve by having your BATNA (Best Alternative to a Negotiated Agreement) in place. This is determining beforehand at what point you walk away if negotiation is not possible. For example, if you are negotiating for a pay rise and your employer will not provide it, a BATNA would be a job offer with another organisation. Your negotiating leverage with your current employer is greatly enhanced if he or she recognises that you are in demand somewhere else.

Lastly, preparing well for an important negotiation involves *rehearsing*. Ury suggests rehearsing the negotiation like lawyers often rehearse tough court cases: talking it through with a colleague or friend. This has the advantage of ensuring you really do prepare and also gives you insight into what the other may do during the negotiation. You will also gain confidence as well as insight into your body language and the tone of your voice. Finally, role playing allows you to practise different scenarios and be ready for them once you are in the negotiation.

In the negotiation

Preparing well is essential, though in itself it is not enough. You must also perform and deliver in the negotiation. The following tips may be helpful:

- *Ask questions*: Good questions can help you understand the other party's point of view. Evidence shows that successful negotiators ask twice the number of questions and spend over twice the amount of time acquiring and clarifying information than average negotiators. The more you know, the more likely you are to find a solution satisfying to you and agreeable to the other parties.

- *Listen actively and respond*: Active listening refers not only to the words themselves, it includes being aware of the intentions, motives, concerns and considerations embedded in the answers given. Active listening also requires some repeating of what was said, reflecting what was intended and commenting on implications for you and others. It should demonstrate respect and genuine engagement with others around the table. Repetition and signalling agreement can prevent misunderstandings and be very effective in building consensus ('I support that...'); acknowledgement can demonstrate your empathy without signalling your agreement ('I appreciate you're anxious about...'). If you vehemently disagree with something said and do not even want to show acknowledgement, then you can reflect ('There seems to be extreme concern that...'). Here, you have actively responded, though you have not indicated that you regard their point as legitimate.

- *Do not react*: Ambrose Pierce famously advised 'Speak when you are angry and you will make the best speech you will ever regret'. When faced with an angry person or escalating conflict, the natural impulse is to react instinctively. This often escalates the conflict and in such circumstances, objectivity is lost. Real interests are forgotten and people fall back on entrenched positions. It is essential to regain composure: Step back, take time out from the situation, know what sets you off – your 'hot buttons' – and recognise when someone is pressing them. Pause and use silence to regain perspective. Replay the conversation back to gain time. Never make decisions on the spot when you are being attacked.

- *Help others to save face*: You may find yourself in a situation in which someone else has made the speech which they regret. It may be possible to help them to back away without feeling like they are backing down. Allow tempers to cool slowly by silence or speaking slowly. Acknowledge that the issue being discussed is an emotional one but that there is still opportunity to find a shared solution. It may be useful to agree a 'gold standard' which is a measure of fairness against which options can then be compared so that what is finally decided is both reasonable and achievable.

- *Sit next to the other party*: Sometimes there is value in sitting on the same side of the table, establishing a sense that the shared problem (and hopefully the solution) is on the other side. This is similar to sitting next to a patient or family member when discussing a difficult diagnosis or decision, rather than sitting opposite.

Closure and commitment to a lasting relationship

If one party believes that the outcome of the negotiation is not fair, in the long run the negotiation cannot be considered a success.

Within the healthcare organisation in which you are working, it is likely that you will have repeat negotiations with those that you work with. Reputations are built through negotiations so you will benefit from building trust in ongoing relationships, rather than building a reputation as someone who goes for the quick and inconsiderate solution. Your reputation will follow you to each of your subsequent interactions.

There is no negotiation method or technique that can help you if you do not bring integrity to the table. Integrity is at the heart of what we do in healthcare and it must be present at the negotiation table if it is to be present in our work.

References and further reading

Blake, R. and Mouton, J. (1984) *Solving Costly Organizational Conflicts: achieving Inter-group Trust, Cooperation, and Teamwork.* Jossey-Bass, San Francisco.

Marcus, L. J., Dorn, B. C., Kritek, P. D., Miller, V. G. and Wyatt, J. B. (1995) *Renegotiating Health Care: Resolving Conflict to Build Collaboration.* Jossey-Bass, San Francisco.

Shell, R. (1999) *Bargaining for Advantage: Negotiation Strategies for Reasonable People.* Penguin, London.

Spurgeon, P. (2001) Staying afloat. *Health Service Journal,* **27**, September.

Ury, W. (1993) *Getting Past No: Negotiating your Way from Confrontation to Cooperation.* Bantam Books, New York.

CHAPTER 12

Developing future clinical leaders

Oliver Warren and Ruth Carnall

Career progression within the NHS has traditionally been based on technical and academic ability at the expense of the so-called 'softer' attributes, such as emotional intelligence, discussed in preceding chapters. As a result of this, good clinical leaders have not always been identified, nurtured and developed by the system in which they work, but have emerged due to a mixture of their own ability, self-motivation, luck and patronage. This has led to significant variation in the standards of clinical leadership within and between different NHS organisations and has impacted on the standard of care provided to patients. The inquiries and resulting reports into clinical negligence at Bristol, Alder Hey and Maidstone and Tunbridge Wells Trusts all highlighted organisational deficiencies in clinical leadership.

This chapter looks at how we might support the development of future clinical leaders that the system requires. It details some of the many methods that can be used to develop leadership, with a particular emphasis on the role of mentoring, as a result of the authors' experiences of both delivering a leadership scheme in which mentoring is a key component and participating in a mentoring relationship together.

In order to develop effective clinical leaders, the NHS and its stakeholder organisations must place professional and personal development of clinical staff at the centre of their priorities, since clinical leaders are unlikely to emerge without creating an environment in which their skills have been nurtured and are valued.

There is considerable debate in the literature as to whether leaders are born or whether they can be made. Whilst Kotter (1990) argues that leadership consists of a series of definable skills that can and should be taught, others have suggested that there must be a prerequisite level of innate natural leadership ability. Regardless of this debate, there is little contention that whilst certain individuals and personality types appear to take to leadership roles more readily, all professionals can develop their ability to lead others and can learn some of the techniques and behaviours that are essential for effective leadership. However, at what level leadership development for clinicians should occur, and whose responsibility it is, is a matter for discussion. There is no single 'right' way.

This book holds that all clinicians, regardless of career stage, have a duty to assess what leadership development they require and seek opportunities to receive it. This might be in the form of in-house training, courses, schemes, professional qualifications or work placements, as discussed in preceding chapters (see in particular Chapters 7, 8 and 9).

Clinical leadership development cannot, though, be entirely left to the individual; all NHS organisations require strategies addressing the needs of leaders at all levels, including doctors, and there are some excellent examples of local organisations which place a real focus on developing medical staff to take on senior leadership roles. Currently, however, there is little incentive for primary and secondary care trusts to invest significantly in the leadership development of junior doctors specifically, since they transition frequently between organisations and will in all likelihood not take up permanent consultant or GP partner posts within their current organisation. As a result, the responsibility for leadership development of junior doctors is increasingly falling to Strategic Health Authorities (SHAs) and their partner Deaneries, with an element of oversight, coordination and contribution from national organisations such as the National Leadership Council, Medical Education England, the Conference of Postgraduate Medical Deans of the United Kingdom (COPMeD) and the Academy of Medical Royal Colleges. The SHAs and Deaneries are carrying out a number of functions to this effect, including:

- Embedding leadership and management skills into the regular appraisal and assessment processes of all trainees
- Commissioning (and less frequently providing) leadership development schemes and courses for trainees
- Talent management of future medical leaders – in other words prioritising those with the greatest potential for leadership and development opportunities
- Ensuring the environment is supportive of, and conducive to, trainees taking Out of Programme Experiences (OOPE) to develop medical management and leadership skills
- The provision of opportunities such as Medical Leadership Fellowships, or international placements in medical management in developing countries (see Chapter 13).
- Designing and executing inclusion strategies to ensure representation of all medical backgrounds within leadership positions

The methodologies available for leadership development are vast, ranging from self-directed learning using books and audio recordings, to one-to-one coaching, residential courses, diplomas and degrees (see Chapter 7 on education and training). For some people, learning occurs alone and is entirely self-directed, whereas for others it occurs in teams or as part of a cohort recruited to schemes, programmes or fellowships. Before any individual clinician or associated organisation commissions a package of leadership development they must have clarity on what it is they are seeking to achieve.

For an organisation, such as a Deanery or SHA, it is essential to clarify what the specific aims of any programme or scheme are. Is it to develop a large cohort of junior doctors through a broad inclusive programme such as a scheme for all General Practice trainees? Or is it to develop a cohort of high-potential future clinical leaders through a more targeted approach involving assessment of potential and competitive recruitment? Proponents of both approaches exist and neither is 'wrong or right'; they simply address different strategic challenges. However, it is critical to make a decision in the knowledge that the choice made will affect the methods that are possible and appropriate for leadership development to occur. For an individual clinician, the issues of cost, time commitment and provider reputation are important, as are the true learning opportunities and sustainability of any development.

Once participants on any given programme, scheme or course have been confirmed, regardless of selection method, an assessment of each individual's learning needs should be made. This allows those providing leadership development to tailor their approach, while also enhancing the self-awareness of the participant and helping people to monitor their own progress. A range of diagnostic tools are available to help individuals self-assess their leadership skills, and superiors, colleagues and reports can also be involved in any assessment by utilising a 360-degree appraisal mechanism. Individual participants can be encouraged to express their own personal aims and expectations and these can then be aligned alongside the sponsor organisation's strategy, culture and human resources management.

Leadership schemes and courses have a definite part to play in developing leadership skills for clinicians. To ensure maximum benefit, it is important for the participating individual or team to use 'real-life' challenges facing them and their organisation as case-study material to be explored within some of the sessions. Further gain is made when programmes are relatively lengthy in duration and combine formal training ('classroom') with experiences on the job ('field'). The evidence is clear that adults learn best when 'training' is an active experience, interspersed with periods of reflection – real work, linked into career progression and the next wave of professional challenges. However, this type of leadership development tends to be expensive.

Purchasing on an individual basis one of the plethora of two- or three-day courses available in the marketplace can be interesting and beneficial and can significantly improve the knowledge base of participants with regard to health-care systems, processes, structures and governance. However, this 'piecemeal' approach is likely to have limited long-term effect on individuals' leadership behaviours (as discussed in Chapter 10), particularly once they return to their day jobs. Furthermore, it is unlikely to catalyse large-scale service improvement because crucially such courses do not provide the opportunity for participants' organisations and services to develop alongside them.

The leadership development methodologies listed below, whilst only a sample, are the most frequently utilised within leadership programmes in healthcare. Over the last two years, the authors of this chapter have been involved in the commissioning and delivery of leadership development programmes for junior doctors, and have participated throughout their careers in leadership and management schemes, mentoring, coaching and action learning sets. The following methods are derived largely from our personal experience.

Mentoring

Mentoring has been defined as

> off-line help by one person to another in making significant transitions in knowledge, work and thinking

and elsewhere as

> a form of human development where one person invests time, energy and personal know-how in helping another person grow and improve to become the best that he or she can become.

Mentoring can bring significant benefits to the mentee, the mentor and the organisations and systems they work for, and these benefits have been reported for several decades in the management and business literature. *Formal* mentoring has been used in both the private and, more recently, public sectors to support the development of people throughout their careers and ensure that organisations are developing future leaders. Most of the research into mentor–mentee relationships has examined the benefits of mentoring to the mentee, finding that mentoring is related to important career outcomes, such as job satisfaction. It is because of such evidence that many corporate organisations have encouraged mentoring relationships between organisational members. Less work has been carried out to evaluate the beneficial effects for the mentor and for the organisations supporting these relationships. This is probably due in part to the complexity of assessing and defining both what is or is not a mentoring relationship, and what may be appropriate outcomes to measure.

The medical literature on mentoring remains relatively sparse, but anecdotally, mentoring within medicine has traditionally been an *informal* process, occurring spontaneously between junior doctors and their seniors. These uni-professional arrangements tend to be associated with a high level of satisfaction, as they are often based on mutual respect and admiration, and on shared goals and values. However, increased clinical, research and administrative demands and the modernisation of medical career pathways have eroded the opportunities for these traditional mentor–mentee relationships to be established. And where they are established, they are not without disadvantage: mentors are often inextricably linked to the appraisal, assessment and future prospects of the mentee; mentors may have competing interests and agendas, and potentially can impose their viewpoints on workplace issues and culture. Furthermore, traditional medical mentoring has tended to centre on clinical skill development, rather than the wider set of leadership and management capabilities required to be an effective consultant or GP. Finally, on occasions, mentorship may have been less accessible to minority groups, such as women or black and minority ethnic trainees. These factors mean that if mentoring is to be utilised as a leadership developmental tool for clinicians, attention must be paid to its potential limitations and a more formalised process to establish mentor–mentee pairings should at least be considered.

Aspiring clinical leaders can benefit greatly from seeking to establish a mentoring relationship to help them develop both personally and professionally. What form this might take and with whom is very much down to the individual concerned. Some might opt to identify potential mentors by talking to senior colleagues or by approaching senior leaders in the organisations in which they work and train. Others will enlist in the formal mentoring schemes. The mentor may be of the same professional background or from a different one, but should always have some experience in developing others and be truly interested in investing the time and energy required to be a mentor (see Table 12.1).

In our role commissioning and delivering NHS London's Prepare to Lead scheme we have witnessed clear benefits to the mentees through being mentored by senior non-medical leaders (or, where medical, now occupying a predominantly managerial role). It has proved to be enlightening for both sets of participants, providing a view into each other's world and bringing a very different perspective to the mentees' issues. Furthermore, it allows for truly 'offline' support and advice where mentees are able to discuss freely their fears, doubts or concerns regarding their career options and choices without fear of appearing uncommitted to their current route. we know that many mentees feel unable to do this when mentored by direct supervisors. Finally, many opportunities have been created through and around the scheme that have not traditionally been open to someone working at a registrar level. These include attending high-level meetings, taking on advisory roles, and the opportunity to impact the management and policy decision-making process in various other ways.

Table 12.1 The ideal characteristics of a mentor.

- Holds a relatively senior position with good access to both contacts and information

- Has clear learning goals of their own from the mentoring relationship.

- Able to communicate clearly and question appropriately to elicit ideas and help the mentee make linkages and reach conclusions

- Helps the mentee gain insights from their reflections, without being judgmental

- Able to challenge traditional approaches and encourage creative and innovative thinking

- Able to help the mentee with analysis and taking a strategic perspective on issues

- Trustworthy and able to hold confidences

- Ensures the mentee retains responsibility for determining outcomes and solutions

- Listens actively, and is able to pick up verbal and non-verbal cues

- Willing to devote sufficient time, energy and commitment

- Has enthusiasm for developing and nurturing talent

- Is approachable and constructive and offers a sensitive, responsive balance between support and challenge

- Is successful in their own right with a wide range of experience

The two authors of this chapter have been in a mentee–mentor relationship for two years, and have found it mutually beneficial, stimulating and rewarding. Subjects frequently discussed in our mentoring sessions include:

- Career aspirations and career planning over the short, medium and long term
- Management of difficult relationships in the workforce
- Delivery of previously agreed goals.
- Project management and leadership challenges currently facing the mentee (or mentor)
- The impact and management of political factors in delivering healthcare
- Personal life issues and events

Finally, it is important for those in mentoring relationships to consider frequently the ongoing benefits of continuing to meet, the stage at which the relationship is at, and whether it remains useful for both involved. A 'no-fault' divorce clause, set up at the start of any relationship, is wise since it facilitates a trouble-free exit from the relationship at any point should either party no longer feel willing or able to participate.

Coaching

Coaching, especially for senior leaders, has been expanding over the last few years. By contrast to the breadth of mentoring, coaching is aimed at performance enhancement in a specific area and is focused on one-way benefit for the coachee. Coaching is goal-orientated and tends to happen over the relatively short term. Goals are usually agreed between coach and coachee, with the coach having overall ownership of the process. There is as yet insufficient research looking at what happens in the coaching process that can inform leadership development more broadly – why coaching is successful in some settings and not in others, and what sort of leaders benefit most from coaching. Both the authors have received coaching, and found it useful, although benefits may vary according to professional circumstance and the relationship formed with the coach in question. Junior clinicians generally have little opportunity to access this leadership development resource (in part this may be due to the significant cost per person involved), although organisations are beginning to offer coaching for more senior clinicians when appointed to new leadership roles. Coaching is occasionally incorporated into leadership schemes for junior doctors, such as NHS London's Darzi fellowships and the Health Foundations schemes described in Chapter 8.

Action Learning

Action Learning is based on the notion that leadership knowledge, skills and attitudes can be developed through the joint problem-solving of issues that arise in the work place, during real-life projects, and by observing and working with others. Not only can learning occur, but the individual whose issues are being focused on at any one time can, by working through them in a safe, supportive and facilitated environment, gain valuable insight and reassurance, and can formulate plans to take issues forward. Typically, an Action Learning 'set' consists of six to eight individuals with a common purpose or interest, be that their workplace, sponsor organisation or beliefs, accompanied by an experienced facilitator. Participants will request time-slots to air an issue that they wish to work through and address, and then, through a mixture of open questions, appreciative enquiry, role play and alternative perspectives, seek to address the issue in a structured way. The aim is not to give advice (tempting as this can be) but to help and empower the individual in question to reach their own conclusions.

Two important factors for a successful Action Learning set are, firstly, trust across all its members, and secondly, that everyone focuses fully on helping the person whose issue is being explored at any given time (rather than any other agenda they may have). Reflection can often help various members of the group learn from others' problems and challenges, particularly where individuals are working on similar improvement or change projects in different organisations or within similar environments.

Networking

Networking can play an important part in leadership development and, when successful, networks may be sustained over a longer period than coaching or even mentoring. Networking is difficult to define but tends to involve the creation of interdependent, often mutually beneficial relationships. It can occur formally, for example by participating in national groups or being an active member of a society, or informally, by getting to know, interact and then work with others who share a common purpose or interest in similar issues.

The impact of networking can be very powerful, but the creation of networks requires not only a significant and conscious effort by the individual, but also support and help from the organisation or group with whom they work. We have witnessed networking occurring in two distinct ways within the leadership development schemes in which we have participated or delivered:

- **Peer networking – the cohort effect**
  Expressing an interest in leadership positions and developing leadership abilities can bring with it some risk. Nowhere has this been truer than in clinical leadership, where claims of 'going over to the dark side', although diminishing, are still heard. This can lead to a sense of isolation. Establishing a network of like-minded individuals, who can support, encourage and provide opportunities for each other not only to learn and develop but also to take on new roles or leadership positions can have pronounced effects, diminishing the sense of isolation and making individuals feel part of a team or movement. Combining individual expertise and energy can result in achieving projects that would have previously felt unattainable to individual participants.

■ **Networking with senior leaders**

Networking with senior leaders, who may be mentors or group sponsors, can provide opportunities to experience and witness interactions and events to which individuals may not normally be privy. Senior leaders often provide a wide range of contacts and so can deepen and extend networks as well as offering a more diverse range of perspectives, views and information. Networking and learning with senior leaders allows those more junior to increase their own profile and those of their organisation and colleagues. This may bring further opportunities to contribute and be involved in key decision-making. Finally, it is prudent for any future clinical leader to establish a network of supporters and senior leaders around them, rather than rely on the patronage of a single mentor or senior sponsor. This is firstly because relationships change, and over-reliance on any single individual can create dependency and subservience. Secondly, for those who aspire to lead in different organisations and regions and at different levels of healthcare (local, regional, national and international), it is unlikely that any single individual can provide all the opportunities and experiences required to progress. For these reasons, aspiring clinical leaders will do well to surround themselves with varied networks of senior leaders.

Experiential learning

For true learning about leadership and the management of others to occur, the authors advocate that at least some of this learning should be experiential. New roles or 'stretch assignments' offer important development opportunities. These challenges require the individual to work outside their comfort zone in order to learn new skills, knowledge and behaviours which can take many forms, including entirely new jobs, secondments to other organisations, or part-time roles alongside ongoing clinical work. As has been previously discussed (Chapter 8), Medical Leadership Fellowships for junior doctors (known as Darzi Fellowships in London) typically last one year and require participants to take an 'Out of Programme Experience' to work within trusts on quality improvement projects and service redesign. The Chief Medical Officer's Clinical Advisor Scheme, run from the Department of Heath but involving other partner organisations provides another excellent opportunity for junior doctors to take time away from clinical work and experience public health, medical management and patient safety challenges. However, not all stretch assignments require stepping out of clinical work. Much (often more) can be learned by balancing clinical work alongside contributing to other projects or working part-time in another capacity. A number of participants on the Prepare to Lead scheme have worked as clinical advisors to projects alongside their day jobs, including the Polyclinic Project, the Local Hospital Project and the End of Life pathway at Healthcare for London, and with external agencies such as the Judge Business School at Cambridge University and consultancies.

Conclusion

As the NHS moves into its next era, clinical leadership will become more important than ever before. The development of high-quality clinical leaders for the future will not occur by accident. The system as a whole and the organisations which together make up the systems must play an important role. But equally, it is the responsibility of every clinician to shape his or her own development as a leader. Leadership skills can be developed in a number of ways, but if we are to create a generation of clinicians able to take on key leadership roles within their organisations and beyond, then opportunities to participate in formal leadership schemes involving the techniques discussed in this chapter are of critical importance.

References and further reading

Berwick, D. M. (2003) Improvement, trust, and the healthcare workforce. *Quality and Safety in Health Care*, **12**, 448–52.

Bristol Royal Infirmary Inquiry (2001) *Learning from Bristol: The Report of the Public Inquiry into Children's Heart Surgery at the Bristol Royal Infirmary 1984–1995*. The Stationery Office, London.

Burke, R. J. and McKeen, C. A. (1989) Developing formal mentoring programs in organizations. *Business Quarterly*, **53**, 76–99.

Clutterbuck, D. (1992) *Everyone Needs a Mentor*. IPM, London.

Darzi, A. (2007) *Healthcare for London: a Framework for Action*. NHS London, London.

Darzi, A. (2008) *High Quality Care for All: NHS Next Stage Review Final Report*. Department of Health, London.

Fagenson, E. A. (1989) The mentor advantage: perceived career/job experiences of protégés versus non-protégés. *Journal of Organizational Behavior*, **10**, 309–20.

Flaherty, J. (1999) *Coaching; Evoking Excellence in Others*. Butterworth-Heinemann, Boston, MA.

Ham, C. (2003) Improving the performance of health services: the role of clinical leadership. *Lancet*, **361**, 1978–80.

Hartley, J. and Hinksman, B. (2003) *Leadership Development: A Systematic Review of the Literature*. NHS Leadership Centre, London.

Healthcare Commission (2007) *Investigation into outbreaks of* Clostridium difficile *at Maidstone and Tunbridge Wells NHS Trust*. Commission for Healthcare Audit and Inspection, London.

Health Foundation (2009) Health Foundation Leadership Fellows. http://www.health. org.uk/current_work/leadership_schemes/leadership_fellows.html (accessed 10 March 2009).

Kram, K. E. (1988) *Mentoring at Work: Developmental Relationships in Organizational Life*. University Press of America, New York.

Kotter, J. (1990) *A Force for Change: How Leadership Differs from Management*. Free Press, New York.

Levinson, D. J., Darrow, C. N., Klein, E. B., Levinson, M. H. and McKee, B. (1978) *The Seasons of a Man's Life*. Ballantine, New York.

Redfern, M., Keeling, J. W. and Powell, E. (2001) *The Royal Liverpool Children's Inquiry Report*. The Stationery Office, London.

NHS Institute for Innovation and Improvement, Academy of Medical Royal Colleges (2008) *Medical Leadership Competency Framework*, 2nd edn. http://www.insti- tute.nhs.uk/images/documents/MLCF%20May%202009.pdf (accessed 7 March 2009).

NHS London (2009) NHS London's Darzi Fellowships. http://www.london.nhs.uk/ what-we-do/developing-nhs-staff/leading-for-health/darzi-fellowship (accessed 8 March 2009).

NHS London (2009) Prepare to Lead. http://www.london.nhs.uk/what-we-do/devel- oping-nhs-staff/leading-for-health/prepare-to-lead (accessed 7 May 2009).

Poole, A. (2003) The implications of Modernising Medical Careers for specialist reg- istrars. *British Medical Journal*, **326**, 194.

Roche, G. R. (1979) Much ado about mentors. *Harvard Business Review*, **57**, 14.

Warren, O., Humphris, P. and Bicknell, C. (2009) 'Prepare to Lead'; Reflections on the first year of a Leadership Development Mentoring Programme for Specialist and GP Registrars in London. *International Journal of Clinical Leadership* (in press).

Whitely, W. (1991) Relationship of career mentoring and socioeconomic origin to managers' and professionals' early career progress. *Academy of Management Journal*, **34**, 331–51.

CHAPTER 13

Leadership and global health

Rebecca Syed Sheriff and Andrew J. M. Leather[1]

So far this book has concentrated on the NHS, but the challenges of global health are, of course, orders of magnitude greater. The NHS's clinical leaders have the opportunity to make a difference to global health as well as health in the UK. This chapter defines global health and global health challenges, outlines the effects of globalisation and the importance of meeting global health needs and describes the changing political climate. In addition, the ways of getting involved in leading global health initiatives alongside regular training are discussed, together with a case study describing the partnership between two hospitals in the UK and Africa.

Former South African president Nelson Mandela may be the pre-eminent example of a global leader, and in his presidential inaugural speech, Mandela (1995) said:

> Our deepest fear is not that we are inadequate. Our deepest fear is that we are powerful beyond measure. It is our light, not our darkness that most frightens us. We ask ourselves, who am I to be brilliant, gorgeous, talented, fabulous? Actually, who are you not to be? You are a child of God. Your playing small does not serve the world. There is nothing enlightened about shrinking so that other people won't feel insecure around you. We are all meant to shine, as children do. We were born to make manifest the glory of God that is within us. It's not just in some of us; it's in everyone. And as we let our own light shine, we unconsciously give other people permission to do the same. As we are liberated from our own fear, our presence automatically liberates others.

Mandela is challenging us to overcome our insecurities and inadequacies and to 'shine'. This chapter challenges readers interested in global health to shine on the stage of global health, not only as clinicians, but also as clinical leaders.

---

1 The authors wish to acknowledge the help of Kirsten Scott, a medical student at King's College Hospital in the writing of this chapter.

Global health challenges are immense, with the combined problems of significant health needs, lack of resources and the requirement for extensive coordination and cooperation between countries, disciplines and sectors. Increasing globalisation can have positive as well as negative effects on health and health systems. The political climate is changing and UK health professionals are being encouraged to use their experience and skills to help meet global health needs. Effective leadership in global health requires several elements: a foundation of theoretical training, practical experience, effective mentoring and collaborative leadership capabilities.

Global health is a concept that has recently become fashionable. Like 'globalisation', the term 'global health' is widely used but rarely defined. It is most closely related to public health and international health. As with any concept, definition is not only the key to communication but is also important for identifying the problems and solutions that apply to global health. Global health was defined in the *Lancet* (Koplan *et al.*, 2009) as

> an area for study, research and practice that places a priority on improving health and achieving equity in health for all people worldwide. Global health emphasises transnational health issues, determinants and solutions; involves many disciplines within and beyond the health sciences and promotes interdisciplinary collaboration; and is a synthesis of population based prevention with individual level clinical care.

Many nations face the longstanding problem of communicable diseases and an increasing burden of non-communicable diseases exacerbated by high rates of population growth and the associated rising demand for health services. There are increasing numbers of deaths and injuries caused by environmental hazards, lack of health and safety precautions, and violent conflict.

The discrepancy between health needs and resources is known as the 'treatment gap' and leads to alarming health statistics demonstrating the inequalities between high and low/middle income countries. In 2006, 9.7 million children died before reaching their fifth birthday. Of this total, 4.8 million were in sub-Saharan Africa. In sub-Saharan Africa, a woman's lifetime risk of maternal death is 1 in 22, compared with 1 in 8,000 in industrialised countries. Life expectancy for a woman in sub-Saharan Africa is 46 years, compared with 78 years in the UK.

In terms of resources, there is a crisis in staffing health services in countries that are most in need. According to the World Health Organization (WHO), an additional four million health workers (including support workers and managers) are required to fill gaps in the 57 countries with the greatest needs. WHO states that sub-Saharan Africa has 11% of the world's population and 24% of the global burden of disease, yet has only 3% of the world's health workers. The problem is compounded in that the relevance of existing research to the world's poorer nations is questionable. Only 10% of the total spent on health research is directed towards the diseases which are responsible for 90% of the global burden of disease.

Although globalisation has different meanings and implications depending on the field being discussed, the most relevant to health professionals is the following, proposed by WHO (2009):

Globalisation, or the increased interconnectedness and interdependence of people and countries, is generally understood to include two inter-related elements: the opening of borders to increasingly fast flows of goods, services, finance, people and ideas across international borders; and the changes in institutional and policy regimes at the international and national levels that facilitate or promote such flows.

Globalisation can bring great benefits to both rich and poor. In health specifically, it has the potential to increase interconnectedness between health systems so that health and health policy insights have greater transfer across borders. Globalisation also brings about opportunities for greater dissemination of information and collaborative research both between countries and between sectors.

But equally globalisation can have harmful consequences. The negative effects of globalisation include its potential to undermine the authority of nations to govern their own affairs, and the potential for economic and social harm in low-income countries. WHO (2009) states that:

globalisation is putting the social cohesion of many countries under stress, and health systems, as key constituents of the architecture of contemporary societies, are clearly not performing as well as they could and as they should.

The interaction between globalisation and health is complex. Globalisation affects health in a variety of ways, including effects on trade, travel, migration and communications. On a practical level, globalisation increases the complexity of the international health architecture and makes a coordinated approach to global health needs increasingly challenging. However, if we accept that globalisation is an unstoppable phenomenon, clinical leaders need to seek ways of maximising benefits and minimising the drawbacks.

Given the dramatic and increasing effects of globalisation it would be naïve to view the health of any country in isolation. As well as the obvious transmission of infectious diseases between countries due to increased travel and migration, the effects of poverty, conflict, illicit drugs and other health-determining factors are also apparent across borders. This has meant that health and health policies within countries have international knock-on effects. Increasingly, care must be paid to the effects of our health and our health policies internationally. In addition, we cannot afford to be complacent regarding global health challenges that affect our own nation's health.

Health organisation and decision-making is increasingly being determined at an international level. This can be regarded as an opportunity for clinical leaders to become involved in influencing health on a broader level. In addition, globalisation brings with it further opportunities for information-sharing and collaboration in research.

There is also an obligation to help meet global health challenges. As with many developed countries, the UK has drawn health professionals away from low- and middle-income countries where such skills are in short supply and critical for the local health system. In 2003, one in three work permits issued to nurses in the UK went to applicants who came from countries where active recruitment is prohibited, mainly in sub-Saharan Africa. The NHS has benefited significantly from the skills brought in from those countries, and carries a responsibility to 'pay back' this debt.

Growing international political and institutional support for global health

In 2000, world leaders along with leading development institutions met at the United Nations (UN) and set out the Millennium Development Goals (MDGs). These are a set of eight priority development targets to be achieved by 2015. Three of the eight goals relate directly to health (child health, maternal health and HIV/AIDS), and one relates to global partnerships. In 2005, the annual G8 summit sought to increase the impetus to achieving the MDGs and to increase resources for Africa. In 2006, WHO reported on the crisis of the global workforce in the world's poorest countries, calling for a significant scaling-up of training and for more efficient use of existing health workers, supported by 'simple, inexpensive measures like improving management and supervision'. WHO set out a ten-year plan in which the countries most affected could, with support, aim to build their health workforces. In 2007, recognising that progress towards reaching the MDGs was off-track, the G8 and WHO jointly appealed to public and other donors to increase support to African Health systems.

UK policy is encouraging more effort to overcome global health challenges

In 2003, the *International Humanitarian and Health Work Toolkit to Support Good Practice* was written by the Department of Health on the advice of England's Chief Medical Officer, Sir Liam Donaldson. This document set out to provide practical advice to encourage well-constructed career breaks from the NHS and to reduce disincentives to gaining experience overseas.

In *Working Together for Better Health* the UK Department for International Development recognised the importance of health, the close relationship between health and poverty and the importance of improving both health and health equity. Within the document, priorities are set out, along with ways of overcoming challenges, including a more coordinated approach, supporting developing countries, developing links between health systems, and other development work.

Around the same time, a former NHS Chief Executive, Lord Crisp, was asked by the Prime Minister and the Secretaries of State for Health and International Development to examine how the UK's health system could be used to help improve health in developing countries. In his 2007 report, Lord Crisp concluded that developing countries need to be able to take the lead, to initiate and own solutions, and that the UK and other developed countries need to support scaling-up of training, education and employment of health workers in developing countries. The report also advocated more rigorous research and evaluation of what works in development, with sharing of information and more efficient use of resources. The Government's response to the 'Crisp Report' also makes the case for the UK to scale up the international availability of UK institutional and professional expertise, and to do this more strategically. It emphasises the importance of supporting and evaluating international health links, and it commissioned an evaluation of existing health links.

Health is Global, written in 2008 by Liam Donaldson (still England's CMO), outlines the effect of globalisation on health and the need for a coordinated UK strategy. In response to this, the British Government published a five-year strategy which emphasises the importance of strong and effective leadership in global health through strengthened and reformed international institutions. The report also outlines the importance of global health, the impact of global health on domestic health, and the importance of a coordinated approach, given the complex organisational and political landscape, and the interaction of health and other areas of public policy.

Case study of leadership in global health

In 2000, King's College Hospital (KCH) commenced an institutional health link with partners in Somaliland, in the Horn of Africa (Leather *et al.*, 2006). The link quickly evolved from supporting EAH alone to supporting one of the Regional Health Boards and a new medical school. The KCH/THET (Tropical Health and Education Trust)/Somaliland Partnership (KTSP) work has led to the development of a UK-wide Consortium working with the Somaliland Government in rebuilding the health sector. In the last two years, KTSP has played a significant part in a number of ground-breaking initiatives. These include: the graduation of Somaliland's first doctors (over 30 doctors by mid 2009); the launch of the Somaliland Internship Programme; the launch of a 15-month Nurse Tutor Training Programme; extensive educational support to four nursing schools; the completion of a pilot Clinical Officer Training course with ongoing support; the significant strengthening of the Somaliland Medical, Nursing and Midwifery Associations; and the continuing development and support of a revolving drug fund in the central government hospital.

An essential skill of a collaborative leader is the capacity to shift from vertical power relationships to more collaborative 'horizontal' power-sharing, and the ability to empathise (see Chapters 4 and 10). These skills are crucial for pursuing goals and building a joint vision. Collaboration with colleagues in Somaliland on an equal footing and an understanding of the health challenges and needs from their perspective has provided the foundation for the link.

In addition, an understanding of the architecture of decision-making both at home and in Somaliland, was essential in overcoming the challenges of starting a link in a post-conflict setting emerging from the effects of a catastrophic civil war. The work of KTSP has passed through phases of being strategic at hospital, regional and now at national level in Somaliland.

Sustaining the link has involved considerable communication with the many health professionals involved in KTSP, with partners within the UK Consortium and with an expansion of partners in Somaliland. It has been necessary to have the King's management team on board from the onset. Through the creation of a hospital-based International Development Unit (IDU), the administrative and managerial base of the link has been strengthened. The KCH Board has supported the development of the IDU by providing a start-up grant.

Essential to the success of this project has been developing and communicating a joint vision and recognition (by both parties) that the benefits of the collaboration are two-way – both EAH and KCH benefit. To measure success, the IDU has studied benefits to individuals, benefits to professionals and benefits to the hospitals. An obvious tangible benefit that has grown from the link has been the development of a portfolio of global health educational opportunities for medical students within KCL which include self-directed special study research modules. It has been essential to take a long-term view; the first trips to Somaliland by King's Health professionals took place in 2000, but due to armed conflict a strategic link could not be formed until 2002. It has also required a mix of rigidity and flexibility, to work to short-term achievable aims whilst keeping the longer-term vision in mind, having the flexibility to adapt to the changing needs of our colleagues in Somaliland as well as changing circumstances with regard to available resources.

Increasingly there are opportunities for UK health professionals from all disciplines to become involved in meeting global health challenges. This can be done through clinical work, teaching and training, management and research. Opportunities arise both in the UK and overseas in various ways, including through institutional health links, volunteering and research collaboration, amongst others. Although Lord Crisp recommended that overseas volunteering should be made easier for NHS staff (for example, by removing career-progression disincentives), as yet there is no formalised training or career path in global health in the NHS. This is all the more surprising as demand for global health training is high among medical students.

As links with the developing world grow stronger and more numerous, global health leaders are needed from all disciplines, including medical professionals. As much of the global health work is about building services and improving health systems, the combination of clinical and leadership skills is disproportionately valuable. Tomorrow's clinical leaders are already emerging from student groups, such as Medsin, and postgraduate groups, such as Alma Mata. Medsin, through the global health education project, advocates for and also delivers educational initiatives at various medical schools. Alma Mata, a UK-based global health network made up largely of recently qualified doctors, also campaigns for more educational opportunities in global health, such as an established career path in global health within the postgraduate curriculum.

In summary, the health effects of globalisation are becoming increasingly recognised and the political climate is becoming more conducive to meeting global health challenges. UK healthcare professionals are becoming increasingly enthusiastic about taking up opportunities in global health and increasingly effective in doing so. As with any specialty, education and development of skills are essential to practising global health effectively. The multidisciplinary nature of global health necessitates training in diverse fields, such as effects of economics and social policy on health.

A strong theoretical preparation for tomorrow's global and clinical leaders, based on the knowledge and competencies included in this book, will enable the UK to contribute effectively to this challenging field in the future.

References and further reading

Ad Hoc Committee on Health Research Relating to Future Intervention Options (1996) *Investing in Health Research and Development – Report of the Ad Hoc Committee on Health Research Relating to Future Intervention Options.* World Health Organization, Geneva.

Brown, G. and Merkel, A. (2007) Joint statement on International Health Partnership. http://www.number10.gov.uk/Page12904 (accessed 4 June 2009).

Buchan, J. and Dolvo, D. (2004) *International Recruitment of Health Workers to the UK: a Report for DFID.* Department for International Development Resource Centre, London. http://www.dfidhealthrc.org/shared/publications/reports/int_rec/int-rec-main.pdf (accessed 7 June 2009).

Crisp, N. (2007) *Global Health Partnerships: The UK Contribution to Health in Developing Countries.* Department of Health, London. http://www.dh.gov.uk/en/Publicationsandstatistics/Publications/PublicationsPolicyAndGuidance/dh_065374 (accessed 23 May 2009).

Department for International Development (2007) *Working Together for Better Health.* DfID, London.

Department of Health (2003) *International Humanitarian and Health Work: Toolkit to Support Good Practice.* Stationery Office, London.

Department of Health (2008) *Global Health Partnerships: the UK Contribution to Health in Developing Countries – the Government Response.* http://www.dh.gov.uk/en/Publicationsandstatistics/Publications/PublicationsPolicyAndGuidance/DH_083509 (accessed 8 April 2009).

DFID Health Resource Centre (2008) *Evaluation of Links between North and South Healthcare Organisations.* Department for International Development, London.

Donaldson, L. (2007) *Health is Global – Proposals for a UK Government-wide Strategy.* Department of Health. http://www.dh.gov.uk/en/Publicationsandstatistics/Publications/PublicationsPolicyAndGuidance/DH_072697 (accessed 29 April 2009).

HM Government (2008) *Health is global: a UK Government strategy 2008-13.* http://www.dh.gov.uk/en/Publicationsandstatistics/Publications/PublicationsPolicyAndGuidance/DH_088702 (accessed 9 May 2009).

Koplan, J. P., Bond, T. C., Merson, M. H., Reddy, K. S., Rodriguez M. H., Sewankambo, N. K., Wasserheit, J. N. *et al.* (2009). Towards a common definition of global health. *Lancet,* **373** (9679), 1993–5.

Mandela, N. (1995) *A Long Walk to Freedom: The Autobiography of Nelson Mandela.* Abacus, London.

Leather, A., Ismail, E. A., Ali, R., Abdi, Y. A., Abby, M. H., Gulaid, S. A., Walhad, S. A. *et al.* (2006) Working together to rebuild health care in post-conflict Somaliland. *Lancet,* **368,** 1119–25.

Medsin (2009a) *Healthy Planet.* http://www.medsin.org/campaigns/healthyplanet (accessed 5 May 2009).

Medsin (2009b) *Where's the Consultation?* http://www.wherestheconsultation.org/ (accessed 16 May 2009).

Spry, E. (2009) *Postgraduate Training in Global Health for UK Doctors: Our Proposals*. http://www.almamata.net/news/content/postgraduate-training-global-health-uk-doctors-our-proposals (accessed 16 May 2009).

Unicef (2007) *Progress for Children: A World Fit for Children Statistical Review*. http://www.unicef.org/progressforchildren/2007n6/indcx_41401.htm (accessed 8 March 2009).

United Nations (2008) *The Millennium Development Goals Report*. http://mdgs.un.org/unsd/mdg/Resources/Static/Products/Progress2008/MDG_Report_2008_En.pdf (accessed 16 March 2009).

van Lerberghe, W., Evans, T., Rasanathan, K. and Mechbal, A. (2008) *The World Health Report 2008 – Primary Health Care – Now More Than Ever*. World Health Organisation, Geneva. http://www.who.int/whr/2008/whr08_en.pdf (accessed 18 April 2009)

World Health Organization (2006) *The World Health Report 2006 – Working Together for Health*. http://www.who.int/whr/2006/en/index.html (accessed 18 May 2009).

World Health Organization (2009) *Globalisation*. http://www.who.int/trade/glossary/story043/en/index.html (accessed 18 April 2009).

CHAPTER 14

Clinical leadership: bringing the strands together

James Mountford

Nothing great was ever achieved without enthusiasm

Ralph Waldo Emerson

This book has taken a tour through the history of the medical profession in the UK and of the NHS (Part 1), has explored what skills and knowledge clinical leaders need in order to be effective (Part 2) and has delved into some of the practical aspects of clinical leadership in depth (Part 3). Here, we revisit the themes of the opening chapter in the light of these insights by reconsidering some fundamentals of clinical leadership: why it matters, what has hitherto held it back in the NHS and why the current era is one of great promise for clinical leadership. We close with a look to the future.

Why do we need clinical leadership?

Healthcare is expensive: most Western countries spend around 10% of their national wealth on healthcare, with the USA spending nearly twice as much. Despite this, healthcare is too often not of high quality. Recent years have seen much greater awareness among both healthcare professionals and the public about serious shortcomings: unusually high mortality rates in certain hospitals, hospital-acquired infections, and medication errors are three weaknesses which have received particular attention. In healthcare (considered as a single industry) we tolerate defect and error rates orders of magnitude higher than are tolerated in other industries, perhaps because disentangling the effects of the disease processes and those of 'care processes' is difficult (bad outcomes happen even when care is world-class) and perhaps because it is only relatively recently that the extent of defects has become clear. A US study (McGlynn *et al.*, 2003) estimated that there are deficiencies in the care of nearly half of patients who are admitted to hospital. Fortunately not all errors lead to harm, but harm is much more common than most of us think: the best data for NHS hospitals suggests that around one in ten patients admitted suffers an adverse event as a result of the care they receive (Vincent *et al.*, 2001). A third of these are serious, leading to ongoing disability or death, and half or more are considered preventable. 'Bad things' can always happen in healthcare, but they happen much less often in the best hospitals.

As this book has argued, clinical leadership is needed to address these cost and quality issues, in part because healthcare is highly complex, and increasingly so. In the past, both healthcare and the organisations designing and delivering it were much simpler. The adage that clinicians look after patients while managers look after organisations had some validity: treatment and diagnostic options were limited, information was hard to come by, the pace was slower. The NHS is now in the era of the hospital 'mega-Trust' with more mergers and alliances to follow in the coming years, and similar consolidation in primary care. In terms of science and medical knowledge we are victims of our own progress: many patients are living many years with several long-term conditions, and the number of diagnostic tests and treatment options seems to grow exponentially. The actual delivery of care is also getting more complex: patients are treated within a few hours for conditions which previously involved several days in hospital, and treatments (like chemotherapy) are increasingly administered in the home or in primary care settings.

New treatments and tests mean new ways to spend money. In a resource-constrained system like the NHS, with a fixed budget, resource allocation tradeoffs are inevitable. A vital issue is: who makes these decisions, with what knowledge and to what priorities?

These questions call for clinical leadership. Chapter 1 discussed the difference between leadership and management, and offered the following definition of clinical leadership:

> Empowering clinicians to have the confidence and capability to continually improve healthcare on both the small and the large scale.

Clinical leadership puts the voice of the clinician – clinicians' expertise and their professional values – into resource allocation decisions. Clinical leadership emphatically does not mean that there is no place for others' voices in such decisions: great leadership teams are made up of people with a variety of perspectives. Resource allocation must be decided in collaboration with those with other expertise (for example, health economists and commissioning experts) as well as elected or other representatives of the local community.

Clinical leadership also puts clinicians' expert knowledge alongside that of others (in this case, principally general managers) in how services are designed, run and improved, so that we get the most out of how we choose to spend scarce resources. But these activities can conflict with a 'traditional' view of a clinician's role and identity. Traditionally, clinicians work one patient at a time: all attention is focused on doing the best by the patient currently 'in the room'. Leadership, by contrast, requires more than this: it requires clinicians to think also about patients in the queue, and to balance patients' needs with the needs of the wider population. Leading takes clinicians away from the front line where care is given – and where often only clinicians can do the job. So we must ask: is it worth the price?

Emerging evidence for the impact of clinical leadership

Before turning to evidence itself, first consider a comparison with other industries: is it desirable to have technical experts involved in the design and running of organisations, in partnership with general managers? Examples of technical experts playing crucial roles on leadership teams abound in both public and private sectors: for example, strategic and operational issues in the armed forces are handled primarily by professionals who themselves have military backgrounds. Head teachers are drawn from the stock of classroom teachers. Academics are central to the leadership of universities. Oil and gas companies, drilling for reserves in some of the world's most inhospitable territories, have geologists and engineers among their leadership at all levels. Many leaders in biotechnology and pharmaceutical companies are life scientists. Across all industries, strong leadership teams are characterised by their mix of experts in general management (operations, strategy, finance and the like) and experts in the technical field in question. When pressure to perform rises, successful organisations in all industries focus on identifying, recruiting and developing leaders who are able to set direction and manage the organisation through times of uncertainty. If clinical leadership *didn't* matter, this would be in striking contrast to what we find in other industries. In fact, the more complex the industry, the greater the need for technical experts to be part of leadership and management – and buying and delivering healthcare is about as complex as an industry can get.

Beyond this comparative argument, evidence for the benefit of clinical leadership is emerging rapidly and in several forms. There are a growing number of examples from both the UK and overseas that performance rises dramatically when a conscious effort is made to make services more clinically led (as discussed in Chapter 1). Data also comes from more formal academic studies. Several US studies examining the performance of medical groups have found that high-performing groups are characterised by their explicit emphasis on bridging the divide between clinicians and general managers, their clear focus on quality and by the organisation's ability to learn from experience (Shortell *et al.*, 2005; Casalino *et al.*, 2003). In the NHS, high-performing hospitals are distinguished by having CEOs who engage clinicians in decision-making and in dialogue (Academy of Royal Medical Colleges, 2007). Service improvements are more likely to succeed when they are more clinically led (National Co-ordinating Centre for NHS Service Delivery and Organisation, 2006).

Finally, a study correlating operational and overall hospital performance with the level of clinical leadership found that the most clinically led hospitals scored up to 50% higher on important dimensions of performance (Castro *et al.*, 2008). This is consistent with anecdotal observations of the benefit of putting clinicians at the heart of leading their services, and equipping them with the skills and support to do so effectively. An example of this is Service Line Management (SLM) (pioneered by Monitor with Foundation Trusts): at the heart of SLM is a new method of financial reporting called Service Line Reporting under which the clinical leader is accountable for both the quality and the cost aspects of their service. In return, the clinical leader has control of how resources are used. A longstanding problem in the NHS has been that clinicians have cared about quality, while cost has been the responsibility of general managers. The process of clinical care has been a sacred 'black box' which only clinicians can see into, while budgets have been the sacred 'black box' of finance departments. Rarely are organisations led well by people who are not also mindful of stewarding resources. And success is almost impossible if those in charge have different objectives.

What has held clinical leadership back?

Three major factors have held clinical leadership back. First, the value of clinical leadership is hard to demonstrate, whereas the costs are readily apparent. Time spent leading and managing (and developing these skills – see Chapters 4–12) is time spent away from delivering patient care, and there is very little reason to do it (or to aspire to be good at it) if you don't see what benefits come from it in the short term. Furthermore, clinicians are rightly trained to be sceptical and to put great store by evidence. As described above, evidence of clinical leadership's value is only now becoming established, and importantly, what evidence we do have does not come in the form which clinicians inherently find robust: most leadership evidence is in the form of case narratives rather than from randomised controlled trials (RCTs) with their reassuring *p*-values. Unlike comparing two treatment options, complex systems with multiple variables are not generally amenable to study by RCTs. Clinicians need to recognise that the method of research enquiry must fit the question being asked, that RCTs are great for some questions but not others, and that 'softer' methods such as those used in social science can be done with equal rigour.

Second, clinicians often have training in leadership and management which is at best only rudimentary, whereas general managers are the 'experts' in running services. In contrast to the continuous apprenticeship in one's clinical specialty, leadership skills today are often taught off-the-job, often outside the organisation, with little clear relevance to what clinicians do day to day (Chapter 12). As this book has shown, leaders are made, not born; the gap between the depth and quality of leadership training offered to aspiring clinical leaders in the NHS today and the training offered by a corporation or by the military highlights the divide the NHS needs to bridge. Developing leaders is expensive, yet corporations which are ruthless about their costs spend millions a year doing it and evaluating how to do it better – they know it is an essential investment in the organisation's near-term future, not a 'nice to have' for the individuals who benefit from it.

Third, the incentives to become a clinical leader are often weak or even negative. For doctors, being trained in leadership and management has not historically led to promotion or to peer recognition, vitally important in a close-knit profession (though recently introduced changes to merit awards and new leadership awards aim to address this). Role models for the medical profession come in several forms – great diagnosticians or technicians, great researchers, great teachers or heads of professional societies – but they are not typically organisational leaders. Doctors who have chosen this path are still sometimes described as having 'gone over to the dark side' (see Introduction and Chapters 1, 7, 8 and 12). Additionally, there is a financial disincentive: managerial pay scales in the NHS are lower than those for doctors, and for many (especially the highest-flying doctors) time spent 'leading' carries an opportunity cost in terms of private practice and research income. Why earn less, put your career progression at risk and earn the disrespect of your peers?

Despite these many obstacles, there are today pockets of outstanding clinical leadership within the NHS. This demonstrates that some clinicians *do* see a clear link between clinically led services and excellent patient care (the clinical leaders-to-be who have collaborated to produce this book are examples of this). Furthermore, embedding elements of leadership and management into undergraduate training (Chapter 7) will help ensure future generations of clinicians to see this link from the earliest days of their medical careers.

Why clinical leadership's time has come

Several forces are coming together which suggest that we will shortly see a significant change in the breadth and depth of clinical leadership across the NHS. These forces either build clinical leadership directly, or create strong incentives for organisations to develop clinical leaders: clinicians who are able and willing to shape and run high-quality, efficient services.

These forces are considered below under four headings: first, specific policy moves to up-scale clinical leadership; second, the current emphasis on quality of care and new capabilities to measure quality; third, greater pressure on organisations to perform; fourth – and likely most important – doctors' own views of the components of professional excellence are broadening to include service leadership and management roles. In short, clinical leadership is becoming a natural – even a desirable – part of what it means to be a doctor.

1. *Policy moves to up-scale clinical leadership*: As discussed in Chapters 7 and 8, there has never been greater enthusiasm in the NHS for clinicians to acquire leadership and management skills. The Academy of Royal Medical Colleges' framework defining clinical leadership competencies is being introduced into under- and postgraduate curricula. Every SHA is required to develop and implement a workforce strategy, including developing clinical leaders (for example, all SHAs are establishing fellowship schemes to give aspiring clinical leaders broadly based apprenticeships in leadership and management).

2. *Emphasis on quality, the measurement of quality and continuous improvement*: The *Next Stage Review* (Darzi, 2008) set out a three-part approach to quality across the NHS: safety, effectiveness and patient experience. Also crucial is the availability of basic management information in a timely, low-cost form: electronic systems are far from universal in the NHS, but where they exist, they allow healthcare to move into the realm of data-driven management for the first time. This has been the norm in most industries for many years. There is a world of difference between searching for medical records to understand how you are doing and having an automatic data-feed to your desktop every morning.

3. *Pressure on organisations to deliver high-quality care efficiently is rising*: The pressure on organisations to perform has never been greater in the NHS. Recent years have seen the introduction of a series of policy measures designed to put 'edge' into the system for both providers and commissioners (see Chapter 3). For example, Payment by Results means providers are paid on the basis of the volume of work they do, which, combined with choice, creates pressure to attract patients. The requirements on provid-

ers to measure and report quality results are rising, and these may influence patient flows (see Chapter 3): examples include Quality Accounts piloted by Foundation Trusts in 2009 and due to be introduced throughout the system in 2010, and the requirement to measure and publish quality outcomes of direct relevance to patients' lives (PROMs: Patient Reported Outcome Measures). PCTs are introducing financial incentives for quality (CQUINs: Commissioning for Quality and Innovation). No longer is meeting all national targets deemed sufficient; providers must go well beyond this minimum standard, demonstrating year-on-year improvement.

4. *Doctors' own identity and definition of professional excellence*: Historically, clinicians themselves have been sceptical about the value of organisational leadership and management. They have sometimes seen their organisation as little more than a place to come to work. But in a world where doctors regard the organisation, its structures, systems and processes, and its capabilities as essential complements to their own clinical skills, the link between working to improve the organisation and improving patient care becomes clear. As such concepts are built into training, starting with undergraduate training, it becomes natural, rather than maverick, for healthcare professionals from all disciplines to bridge the divide and become organisational leaders.

A prescription for the future

The future lies with the readers of this book. If you are a clinician and you want the NHS to deliver the greatest benefit from its finite resources, you must, at least to some degree, become a clinical leader. Clinical leaders are needed not just in hospitals and primary and community care providers: clinical leadership is needed in health policy, public health and commissioning also. If commissioning is to have a real and positive influence over what services are offered if commissioners are able to reward the best providers, commissioning must be clinically led. Clinical leaders must put their voices and values into the way that resources are allocated. And they must ensure the NHS delivers more in the areas that it chooses to allocate resource. If you believe the way your service is currently run can be improved, then as a minimum you too must become a leader of your own practice and that of your local team.

So clinical leadership in this sense is about adding continuous service improvement to the day-to-day job of being a patient-facing clinician (Berwick, 1992). Beyond this, a small number of clinicians will make leadership a major part of their professional identity, and take on formal positions, such as clinical director and medical director. It is important that some of the brightest and most respected clinicians take on these roles. But since the heart of medicine will always be in the doctor/patient interaction, it is even more important that clinical leadership – in the form of understanding and systematically improving your own practice – becomes a natural part of what it means to be a good clinician.

The coming years will put great strain on the NHS: Britain's public sector spending will come under extreme pressure following the economic crisis of 2008/09. The NHS will need to deliver higher quality with the same or fewer resources. If leadership is deciding what to do and mobilising people to do it, and good management is about delivering the maximum possible with available resources, then there has never been a better time to be a clinical leader or manager.

This book advocates a distributed model for clinical leadership. The authors and editors hope the 'leadership mindset', in the form of constantly trying to understand what drives performance and how to improve it, becomes a natural part of what all clinicians do day in, day out. Changing the basic belief inherent in the divide between clinicians who look after patients while managers look after organisations – is the starting point. We now have the evidence that patients do better when clinicians lead, and we are learning how best to equip clinicians with the skills they need to do just that – to lead.

References and further reading

Academy of Royal Medical Colleges (2007) *Enhancing Engagement in Clinical Leadership*.

Berwick, D. (1996) A primer on leading the improvement of systems. *British Medical Journal*, **312**, 619–22.

Casalino, L. *et al.* (2003) External incentives, information technology, and organized processes to improve health care quality for patients with chronic diseases. *Journal of the American Medical Association*, **289**(4), 434–41.

Castro, P., Dorgan, S. J. and Richardson, B. (2008) A healthier health care system for the United Kingdom. *McKinsey Quarterly*, February.

Darzi, A. (2008) *High Quality Care for All: NHS Next Stage Review Final Report.* Department of Health, London.

McGlynn, E. *et al.* (2003) The quality of health care delivered to adults in the United States. *New England Journal of Medicine*, **348**, 2635–45.

National Co-ordinating Centre for NHS Service Delivery and Organisation (2006) *Managing Change and Role Enactment in the Professionalised Organisation*.

Shortell, *et al.* (2005) An empirical assessment of high-performing medical groups: results from a national study. *Medical Care Research and Review*, **62**(4), 407–34.

Vincent, C. *et al.* (2001) Adverse events in British hospitals: preliminary retrospective record review. *British Medical Journal*, **322**, 517–19.

Some acronyms demystified

AMRC (Academy of Medical Royal Colleges) seeks to promote, facilitate and coordinate the work of the Medical Royal Colleges and their Faculties for the benefit of patients and healthcare. The Academy is made up of the Presidents of the Medical Royal Colleges and Faculties.

http://www.aomrc.org.uk/

BAMM (British Association of Medical Managers)

http://www.bamm.co.uk/

BAMMbino (junior doctors division of the British Association of Medical Managers)

http://www.bamm.co.uk/Services/Support_%26_Development/BAMMbino_2007072440/

BMA (British Medical Association) is the independent trade union and professional association for doctors and medical students, with over 140,000 members worldwide.

http://www.bma.org.uk/

CQC (Care Quality Commission) the independent regulator and inspector of healthcare (including mental health) and social care in England. It was formed in April 2009 by merging three separate regulators (including the Healthcare Commission). Note that Monitor is the independent regulator for Foundation Trusts, responsible for authorising FTs and ensuring they stay in compliance with their terms of authorisation.

http://www.cqc.org.uk/

CQUIN (Commissioning for Quality and Innovation) a framework of incentives for quality and innovation by means of which commissioners can reward providers through financial incentives written into contracts. From 2009/10 DH requires that all contracts link quality and quality improvement to payment.

http://www.dh.gov.uk/en/Publicationsandstatistics/Publications/PublicationsPolicyAndGuidance/DH_091443

DH (Department of Health) is the government department responsible for health policy and public health issues in England. DH enacts the will of Parliament through policy design and impelmentation.

http://www.dh.gov.uk/

G8 (or Group of Eight) is a forum, created by France in 1975, for governments of eight nations of the northern hemisphere: Canada, France, Germany, Italy, Japan, Russia, United Kingdom and United States of America. The forum discusses a range of topics of mutual or global concern, including health.

GMC (General Medical Council) is the licensing and disciplinary body for doctors in the UK. It registers doctors to practise medicine and (from November 2009) oversees revalidation to ensure current fitness to practise. The GMC's purpose is to protect, promote and maintain the health and safety of the public by ensuring proper standards in the practice of medicine.

http://www.gmc-uk.org/

MLCF (Medical Leadership Competency Framework) describes a set of leadership and management competencies which doctors are expected to develop at various stages of seniority, starting with undergraduate education. It was developed jointly by the AMRC and NHS III.

http://www.institute.nhs.uk/assessment_tool/general/medical_leadership_competency_framework_-_homepage.html

NHS III (NHS Institute for Innovation and Improvement) assists the NHS in transforming healthcare by developing and spreading new work practices, technology and improved leadership. Its focus is England and Wales.

http://www.institute.nhs.uk/

NICE (National Institute for Health and Clinical Excellence) is best known for evaluation and approval of new drugs where cost-effectiveness is an issue. It also has a public health and care pathway remit.

http://www.nice.org.uk/

PbR (Payment by Results) is a form of payment to providers where payment is based on units of activity (fee-for-service). In the English NHS there is a fixed tariff (price) for each service or procedure (adjusted based on regional costs) creating incentives for providers to reduce costs. The tariff is updated yearly by DH. Over time, more services and procedures are covered by the PbR system (for example, extension to community care). Contrast other payment methods such as capitation (fixed payment based on number of patients covered) and block payments (payment irrespective of volume).

http://www.dh.gov.uk/en/Managingyourorganisation/Financeandplanning/NHS-FinancialReforms/DH_4065236

PCTs (Primary Care Trusts) receive approximately 80% of the total NHS budget in England. They are local commissioners. Their role is to decide what health services a local community needs and they are responsible for ensuring that such services are provided. There are 152 Primary Care Trusts in England, covering the whole of England geographically, each with its own area. Certain specialist services are commissioned separately, on a regional or national basis.

http://www.nhs.uk/ServiceDirectories/Pages/PrimaryCareTrustListing.aspx

PMETB (Postgraduate Medical Education and Training Board) is the independent regulatory body responsible for postgraduate medical education and training. PMETB ensures that postgraduate training for doctors is of the highest standard.

http://www.pmetb.org.uk/

PROMs (Patient Reported Outcome Measures) measure quality of care from the patient perspective. Initially focusing on high-volume elective surgery procedures, PROMs calculate the health gain after treatments using pre- and post-treatment surveys into the patient's health status and quality of life.

http://www.ic.nhs.uk/proms/

SHA (Strategic Health Authorities) sit between the Department of Health and local PCTs and providers in England. There are ten SHAs covering England. Each is responsible for performance managing PCTs and non-Foundation Trust NHS providers and for planning regional health strategy, including workforce needs.
http://www.nhs.uk/ServiceDirectories/Pages/StrategicHealthAuthorityListing.aspx

SLM (Service Line Management) is an approach to management, budgeting and planning pioneered in the UK by Monitor in the Foundation Trust sector which puts clinicians squarely at the heart of leading clinical services. Each service (department) is the equivalent of a business unit, with its own profit and loss and clinical leaders take charge of the development, performance and quality of their services. A key feature is that clinicians are accountable for both quality and cost, and that they have the freedom to control both.
http://www.monitor-nhsft.gov.uk/home/developing-nhs-foundation-trusts/service-line-management-0/

UN (United Nations) is an international organisation founded in 1945 after the Second World War by 51 countries committed to maintaining international peace and security, developing friendly relations among nations and promoting social progress, better living standards and human rights. The organisation now has 192 Member States and although it is best known for peacekeeping, it also has an important role in global health (see also WHO).
http://www.un.org/

WCC (World Class Commissioning) is an annual assurance programme consisting of a set of competencies, with criteria to assess how well each Primary Care Trust is commissioning healthcare. Commissioning is 'local investment to achieve the greatest health gain and to reduce health inequalities, at the best value'.

WHO (World Health Organization) provides leadership regarding global health, shapes the research agenda, sets norms and standards, including evidence-based policy and provides technical support to countries to monitor and assess health trends.
http://www.who.int/

Further reading about the infrastructure of the NHS can be found in:

McCay, L. and Jonas, S. (2009) *A Junior Doctor's Guide to the NHS*. Department of Health, NHS Medical Directorate, London.
http://www.group.bmj.com/group/affinity-and-society-publishing/NHS%20Guide.pdf

Index

BRITISH MEDICAL ASSOCIATION
BMA Library